TWENTY STORIES:

Resilience, Courage and Hope in the Face of Cancer

A Live Life Now Project Book

Richard Calautti

Calautti, Richard

Twenty Stories: Resilience, Courage and Hope in the Face of Cancer

ISBN: 978-0-9946496-8-3 (Paperback)
ISBN: 978-0-9946496-7-6 (Digital Online)

Cover design by Nancy and Andrew Cover, CAN Design, Melbourne, Australia

Also by Richard Calautti

Live Life Now Project:
Cancer Patients Provide Inspiration For Life

Live Life Now Project is a life-affirming self-help book which reminds you of what is really important in life. The printed version is a beautiful coffee table book filled with 235 direct quotes from cancer patients answering 7 key questions about life – it is an emotional and motivational reading experience which reinforces how lucky we are simply to be alive. Cancer patients have provided quotes to remind us of what is truly important in life, enabling the reader to live life now.

Perth, Australia-based researcher Richard Calautti gathered over 2,000 quotes from cancer patients and survivors from around the world over many years, to compile this book of inspirational life messages.

This book is dedicated to my beautiful cousin Carmel Vitale,
who lost her battle with breast cancer on 27 May 2022.
I miss you, and think about you every day.

I also dedicate this book to Max, Leon and Jasmine.
You bring joy and happiness into my life, and I wish you all the health
and happiness that life has to offer. May you always have the courage
to pursue your dreams and the strength to overcome any obstacle
that comes your way. Keep learning, exploring, and growing.

TABLE OF CONTENTS

INTRODUCTION

I started "Live Life Now Project" originally to help all individuals gain a deeper understanding of what truly matters in life. The project aims to achieve this by sharing the wisdom gained from cancer patients, who have faced a potentially life-threatening illness and come to a profound understanding of what's really important as we often lose sight of these facts as we go about our daily tasks and busyness. For many of us "well" individuals who haven't had a cancer diagnosis we robotically charge through our daily lives, complaining about the same trivialities, blind to the fact that our lives could be so much worse and that something like cancer could be waiting around the corner for us.

Cancer patients often undergo a transformative experience that changes their perspective on life. They learn to value their relationships, prioritize their goals, and appreciate the little things. By sharing their stories and insights via quotes on Instagram (@LiveLifeNowProject) and in the first book of quotes (*Live Life Now Project: Cancer Patients Provide Inspiration For Life*), this project continues to help readers, followers and contributors gain a similar perspective and develop a deeper appreciation for the beauty of being alive.

The goal of this project and these books is not only to inspire individuals to live a more fulfilling life but also to provide support for those who are currently battling cancer. By sharing the wisdom of cancer patients and survivors, the project provides comfort and guidance for those who are struggling with their illness, life in general, or needing a source of inspiration or reminder of what's important. Ultimately, the project seeks to create a community of individuals who can support all of us, regardless of our circumstances, in our journey towards a meaningful and fulfilling life.

Cancer is a disease that affects millions of people around the world, regardless of age, gender, location or ethnicity. It doesn't discriminate, and can turn lives upside down, often leaving individuals feeling helpless and overwhelmed. Cancer can be a devastating diagnosis, and it can have a significant impact on both the patient and their loved ones.

However, amidst the pain and struggle, there is also hope and resilience – millions of cancer patients from around the world have bravely fought this disease and emerged stronger and wiser, regardless of the medical outcomes. Sadly, it must be noted, millions have not survived, and left us far too soon.

For this second book, I wanted to tell in-depth stories about the cancer journey from individuals globally. I wanted to meet with them, chat and interview them, then write their story, whilst maintaining the core themes of Live Life Now Project, which is to share quotes and stories in the hope of inspiring others to live their best life and find hope even in the darkest of circumstances.

During the planning process, I decided to commit to three main goals for this book: to speak directly with cancer patients and learn more about their story; to be as global as possible (as much as language barriers would allow); and to cover as many types of cancers as possible. The aim was to speak with 20 cancer patients and document 20 personal stories, which is reflected in the book's title.

As the author of this book, I had the privilege of speaking with 20 amazing cancer patients and survivors from different parts of the world, including Australia, USA, UK, India, Switzerland, South Africa and Norway, just to name a few. Each person I spoke with had a unique story to tell, but all shared a common thread: they were fighters with an unbreakable spirit who courageously faced their diagnosis head-on, and developed strategies for survival that helped them through their journey. And in the process, they learnt valuable lessons about life and changed immeasurably.

I interviewed these 20 individuals via Zoom over an 18-month period during 2021-2022, amidst the COVID-19 pandemic, which made chatting over Zoom on a global scale very easy (time differences aside!).

Each article talks about their struggles, strategies for survival, and the lessons learned about life and cancer through their journey. Their stories are fascinating, heartbreaking and inspiring, offering a glimpse into the lives of people who have faced and fought cancer. These are real people who opened their hearts to me and shared their experience in a way that can help so many others.

It's with pleasure that I honor the 20 people I spoke with in these pages; I'm so grateful that they trusted me, a novice writer, with their story. In fact, after every single conversation with each of the participants, I was inspired to immediately hit the keyboard and share what they'd told me, such was the power of the experience as described by every participant. I was touched by their willingness to share their most intimate thoughts, feelings, and experiences with me, and I hope that their stories will be a source of comfort, inspiration, and guidance to others who are facing cancer or any other difficult challenge in life. These patients have all grappled with fear, uncertainty, and loss, and tapped into an inner strength to keep going.

Since starting Live Life Now Project back in 2009 and receiving quotes and feedback from thousands of cancer patients worldwide, I realized how much we had to learn about living our best lives (myself included). In a world where we idolise sports stars for their efforts on the field, or social media influencers and personalities for "inspiring" us to be our best selves, I'd wondered why cancer patients and people who'd suffered life altering illnesses were never really included in the list of people to look up to. After all, didn't many of them find a way to overcome impossible mental and physical challenges, despite the odds telling them this wasn't possible? Regardless of the outcome, I was convinced cancer patients could teach us a lot about how to appreciate life and be grateful that we are here to breathe and experience life, regardless of our circumstances. To me, these fighters are the real heroes, often forgotten in a sea of social media platforms celebrating fame and glamour.

In these 20 varied stories, some of the people I spoke with were terminal, some had had a swift cancer journey, others had been fighting multiple diagnoses for decades, yet there was little "doom and gloom" in our conversations, even when asked to elaborate on their lowest points. Those moments surely existed, but they were overpowered by an absolute and resolute need to fight and never give up. A mindset shift had to take place in order to keep going and find the energy and courage to fight.

The conversations were unique to each individual; however, many themes were covered including how cancer altered friendships and relationships, personal coping mechanisms during treatment, life post-cancer, and discussions about specific treatment strategies for their cancer. However, remaining faithful to the nature of Live Life Now Project, there was an emphasis on strategies to survive and find the will to get the most out of life even when the statistics weren't in their favour.

When reading these stories, you may be surprised at how some people admitted that cancer ultimately improved their lives. It's also important for me to mention that the contents of this book are not to be taken as medical advice. As a reader, please remember that every cancer journey is unique and specific to the individual – you may not agree with their views or treatment strategies – many have tried and tested multiple methods of treating their cancer and chose a path they felt suited them. In some cases, traditional treatments were followed; in others, alternative treatments were heavily relied upon. As the writer, I'm not condoning, condemning, or judging specific paths taken – my aim was to document each person's journey. I have to say, I was deeply touched by every person I met and spoke with as I compiled these articles. Their openness moved me and their willingness to share made me so grateful.

Each article is time-stamped with the interview date as I wanted to mark these conversations at a specific point in time. Many of these people are active online, helping others by sharing their journey and progress via blogs, videos, books, articles and various social media platforms. A few have become leaders within organizations that are making a huge difference internationally to the lives of cancer patients and within the area of cancer research. Thousands of people have learnt from them and gained life-saving support from the knowledge and experiences they've shared.

These 20 amazing individuals are just a few examples of the millions worldwide who have been diagnosed with cancer and confronted it head-on and shared their inspiring stories – each has made a difference and had a positive impact on the world or those around them. We are blessed to have access to their openness and fearlessness in telling their personal journey. Their experiences serve as a reminder that even in the face of a difficult and scary life-changing diagnosis, there is always hope and that a cancer diagnosis does not always have to be a death sentence. To each of the 20 individuals who agreed to take part in this part of my project, I thank you from the bottom of my heart – I am so lucky to have met you and I feel such deep gratitude for how you have all impacted my life.

I hope this book is a source of courage and inspiration for anyone who is going through a tough time in their life, and that the experiences and insights shared will provide comfort, motivation, and guidance to anyone who is facing cancer or supporting a loved one through their own journey.

Finally, this book is also a testament to the human spirit, the resilience of the human soul, and the will to keep fighting to stay alive and experience all that life has to offer. It's a reminder that, no matter what life throws at us, we can always find a way to keep going, keep fighting, and keep living.

Richard Calautti
May 2023

1. "CALMNESS REQUIRES STILLNESS."

Chris Breen
Sydney, Australia
8 August 2021

Relying on an inner strength and positive attitude were key in helping Sydney-sider Chris Breen, 43, fight through stage 3 bowel cancer, following his diagnosis in November 2019. At such a young age for this type of cancer (which is becoming increasingly common), Chris was blindsided by the diagnosis but pushed ahead in the only way he knew how: by accepting the reality of the situation and strengthening his mindset.

When diagnosed, Chris was at the tail end of a work contract with one of the "big 4" banks in Australia. Thinking the contract would end and he'd be unemployed and financially strained during his treatment, Chris's employer eased his concerns by offering him a permanent contract with a commitment to assist through the daunting cancer journey that lay ahead.

His financial services industry employer provided a support network for Chris, presenting him with an income protection plan and further medical support in the form of a sports physiologist and occupational therapist to help Chris survive the day to day of eight months off work to focus on the surgery, treatment and recovery that were to follow.

Pre-surgery, Chris also went into planning mode, sorting his will and reflecting on the outcomes of family members who'd been through other illnesses, with thoughts of one's mortality featuring strongly at this time. Post-surgery and through the six months of chemotherapy that followed, Chris met and befriended other cancer patients who'd also faced difficult journeys and outcomes – he came to the under-standing that *"there's always someone worse off"*, which became a mantra that helped him cope with the tougher days of treatment.

"Calmness requires stillness" is a quote Chris was once told by a mentor, and the one which he most referred to when his mind went into over-active mode with racing thoughts around the cancer, treatment and survival, particularly when sitting in the chemo chair receiving his regular dose. Calmly staring into space whilst in the chair was his meditation.

Naturally a positive person, Chris developed an even stronger opti-mism through this period of ongoing treatment, telling himself *"I can't afford to be down"* and that he needed to maintain this outlook for the support network that surrounded him. Aside from Zoom and Face Time chats, contact with immediate family members was impossible, impacted by COVID-19 and travel restrictions – Chris lives in Sydney whilst his family is based in Melbourne. Through the help of his part-ner, pet dogs, the support of neighbours, work colleagues and close friends, Chris also had a network to help him push forward in his battle.

His exercise physiologist also taught him the importance of choosing one's mindset, because the right mindset is powerful and will help you through the toughest situations. He set aside mini goals (*"My port comes out on Wednesday, then I can have a shower!"*) that served as a type of reward system to help him come out the other side of every hurdle. During treatment, Chris remained firm about not allowing 'cancer' to take over his mind, he was resolute in pushing ahead and moving forward, stating:

"You choose your mindset – you can choose to sit there and be down or push ahead. Physically, it was difficult at times, so goals were set – I'll just walk to the end of the street at lunchtime, then maybe again later in the day."

Basic household tasks like doing the washing were also included in his set of goals as a way of integrating the physicality back into his life, with Chris advising:

"First pick your mindset, then choose the outcome you're trying to achieve, and break it down into smaller tasks so you can get to that outcome. Mindset is powerful."

Before cancer, Chris would worry about the usual daily things almost every well person worries about, but he now recognises a difference in himself and how much less space he allocates to these matters. He also finds that his days since cancer are more relaxed and less structured or planned than before. The worries around trivial disputes with colleagues or friends are much less – letting things sit to see where they land is an option rather than aiming for the comfort that comes with having every minor grievance totally figured out. There's a relaxed approach to life, concluding: *"Why put yourself through pain and stress and being OCD when you don't need to?"*

Always reasonably laid back as a person, Chris noted that trivial thoughts around *"What will people think of me?"*, *"What did I say?"* and *"What have I done?"* have also started to disappear from his life, with these concerns now falling into the 'small stuff' basket: *"I only worry about what I can control and move ahead from there."* There is sometimes a momentary recognition of this changed attitude, but much of this is now inherent in his daily life and considered a permanent change.

Going through the fears that come with cancer have lifted the bar of what Chris regards as scary in life nowadays. Reflecting back on his journey and the survival that followed have given Chris a feeling that he can get through almost anything now: *"I can push ahead and deal with what life throws at me."*

Chris felt an eye-opening moment in July 2020 when he had received the all-clear from the oncologist, following eight months of surgery and treatment. The oncologist said: *"Come back in six months for a scan, but for now you are a free man."* Oddly, Chris realized that this was one of the most alarming moments in his journey because it meant his life of doctor appointments, chemotherapy sessions, scan-xiety, and treatments was over, and living a cancer-free, normal daily life was now up to him. And, like many cancer patients, in the days since given the all-clear, he wonders with each cough, sneeze or minor sickness: *"Is the cancer back?"* For now, with a more relaxed attitude to life, Chris regards this as the biggest worry he has to contend with.

Still working out what the overall life plan would be, Chris has not had any 'life changing' lightbulb realisations just yet – rather than planning for the future, he's happy to wait for that enlightened and inspired moment where he decides what 'he wants to do with his life.' For now, he's happy with his job and current situation. Even during Sydney's COVID-related lockdowns, there was no rush and he took life day by day:

"The biggest plan I have at the moment is that I want to go back to Hawaii because I love Hawaii, but there's no travel* thanks to COVID. Instead, I look to today rather than five years ahead, because five years ahead may not be there. You've got to make the most of what you've got now."

When it comes to stress and working through life's toughest obstacles, Chris says:

"There's good stress and bad stress. Good stress keeps you on your toes and is healthy. The bad stress leads you to a dark place. How do you break it apart

and get others to see the light in what's ahead of them? You've got to push forward from that."

* Due to COVID-19, Australia experienced ongoing travel restrictions and lockdowns during 2020-2022.

2. "I AM INCREDIBLY GRATEFUL FOR HOW CANCER CHANGED MY LIFE."

Heather Smith
Wisconsin, USA
13 August 2021

When I spoke with lung cancer fighter Heather Smith, it was very early in the day in Perth, Australia and to say that Heather brightened up my morning from our chat would be an understatement. As a life coach who turned her life around three years into her cancer journey, Heather is one of the most positive, life-affirming people I've come across in the years that I've been running Live Life Now Project. Her exuberance for life itself and living it to the fullest with the right mindset, altered my way of thinking and set the tone for my day.

Heather was diagnosed with lung cancer in 2016 at the age of 34 – she has the ALK positive genetic mutation for which there is no cure, and her lung cancer has metastasized to her brain. In August 2019, three years after the initial diagnosis, Heather's disease progressed, and she hit one of the lowest moments in her cancer journey which resulted in a rushed ambulance trip to the hospital following three seizures and cracking her head on the floor of a concrete patio.

This was the turning point for Heather. For the three years prior to this event, she was *'going through the motions'* with cancer, holding on to the day job that she loved as a project manager for an IT company but working 60 hours a week and living a daily life which consisted of waking up, going to work, recovering at night on the couch from fatigue, returning to bed, and then repeating it all the next day.

With the help of a mindset coach, Heather transformed her outlook towards cancer, which set her cancer journey on a new path. Today she calls herself "The Designated Thriver" using self-coaching as an important tool for herself, and also offering coaching to other cancer patients through her "Living Lives with Lung Cancer" website.

Below is the transcript from my conversation with Heather.

Before your shift in mindset in 2019 following the events of August that year, how were you living life as a cancer patient from your initial diagnosis in 2016 until that transformational point in 2019?

At the time I was taking targeted therapy which is like a chemo pill, and the side effects were similar to chemo: fatigue, vomiting, nausea, loss of taste. I was so tired that I just couldn't get off the couch to do anything – work, home, couch, bed, was my routine. That's not a normal 35-year-old person's life, and I started to notice my thoughts were stuck in: *'This is not how my life is supposed to look. This is not supposed to be me.'* At this time, I was living with some level of denial, and I'd become disempowered and disassociated with my own physical existence. I wasn't particularly angry, it just felt like I'd been betrayed by my body. I felt so strongly that this was not what my life was supposed to look like, this wasn't supposed to happen to me and here I was.

At that moment in hospital in 2019, what was the change?

I clearly remember thinking: *'I am not doing cancer right. I am not doing my life right. I haven't been living a life. I'm not doing this very well. I need to be different, and I need to think different. I need to live big.'* So, I set about to change it. And that involved a lot of personal development, and figuring out what really would work for me to become a person that says: *'I am living life now, to the fullest.'*

What did you change at that time?

I remembered the valuable advice of an aunt who had fought breast cancer and kidney cancer, which was: *'You have to take care of your body, you have to move, you have to be mindful of the things you're eating. Move and be strong. And you need to take care of your mental health.'* I was doing none of those things.

After hospital, I realized how much muscle mass I'd lost due to the fatigue and being on the couch for one year. To get my body moving, I started with a 30-day yoga challenge and made a promise to myself to do this every day – even just five minutes was an achievable goal on low energy days. As I dove into it and built up the time and focused on my personal development, I discovered things about my spirituality, and I grew and strengthened that practice and found a coach, then self-coaching and, as a result, changed how I felt about my cancer.

How did a life coach help you, and how has life coaching in general helped you?

I initially joined a number of cancer support groups online, but I didn't find one that spoke to me. They help others, they just didn't work for me. What I found instead was a life coach, not a cancer patient. A life coach worked for me. It helped me clean up how I was thinking about everything, which then meant everything became better in my life. And learning to recognize I can have a shit day and it's ok, it's not permanent. And to not resist feeling badly – when you resist feeling bad, it sticks around longer. If you feel it, it goes away eventually.

Life coaching also allowed me to really embrace the dichotomy of life with cancer, where you have these high moments like when your scans are stable, or the low moments where you're sicker than a dog, hunched over a toilet and you need to go to the ER. That's a crummy day of cancer life. But to experience one fully, you need to experience the other just as fully. And when you limit that by trying to stay positive all the time, you limit yourself from feeling so much deeper and so much more strongly, and that is really unfair. It shrinks your human experience. Now I'm wanting to feel the highest of the highs, and I'm willing, ready and capable of feeling the lowest of the lows. And that has allowed me to live more fully. And it's just been a blast. Cancer life isn't fun but I'm having fun.

As a life coach yourself with your own practice, your clients are cancer patients themselves. What are some of the commonalities you see in their outlook and what they're facing with their cancer?

It's interesting because I see so many people who say: *'I can't plan for a future. I used to have a career but when I was diagnosed, I had to stop work and I was plunged into early retirement.'* It feels like parts of their identity which they have nurtured as they've grown into adulthood have been ripped up and thrown to the ground. They feel very lost and groundless. My job as a life coach is to help find the pieces and put them back together.

Who was your support network, and how important is a support network for cancer patients?

I heard a concept from a mindset coach, which was about creating a 'dream team' of support around you. I took that idea and magnified it for cancer life and have since developed my own dream team of people to support me; they've each been assigned specific roles based on what I need and I have asked their permission to do this – they have an actual role. For example: *'When I have scan-xiety, this is what I need you to tell me, this is your role.'* It helps me as I have the exact support I need, and it helps the supporters give me their support and feel useful.

It's empowering on both sides. Every experience is better because everyone knows what their job is.

Having a support network is very important and you can build it however you like – be resourceful, be creative, think outside the box. You don't have to get support from the people who have the same type of cancer as you, you can get support from other people. You can ask for support from a wide variety of places. If you are able to clearly express your expectations, other people will be able to rise up and say: *'Yes I can do that, I can help you in that way.'* All they want to do is actually help you. Ask for the help, accept the help.

What advice would you give to 'well' individuals about what they should and shouldn't say to a cancer patient?

From my perspective, one of the worst things you could say is *'You don't look sick'* because you don't know what's going on underneath for a person. Another is *'You should/should not do/take this thing'* when they might be peddling snake oil or recommending high doses of turmeric, and *'You should never eat sugar'* is also another pet-hate of mine. It also diminishes someone's experience with cancer by saying *'My aunt had cancer and she's fine now.'* It may have been a different type of cancer but that type of comment doesn't help a cancer sufferer in that moment. Be willing to ask what the person needs to feel supported. Sometimes they don't want positivity, right then and there, it's very respectful to ask what they need.

The other thing I see so very often is people will tell you as a patient: *'Just be positive! You've got this! You're going to kick cancer's ass!'* Well, the truth is that, in some cases, you're not going to kick cancer's ass, it's not going to go away, you may live with it forever. There's a lot of fake positivity: *'I need to think positive; I need to think happy thoughts'* and that is disingenuous to the human experience where life is just 50/50 – there are really good times, and there are really bad times. And there's not a space where you can go to have a bad day in cancer life without somebody trying to make it better, and sometimes you just need to be miserable. You just need a space where you can go and be heard and understood, deeply and truly, from one cancer patient to another.

In November 2019, you provided this quote to our project in response to the question "What has your illness taught you about life?" You responded with: *"It's all about your mindset. Love large. Love harder. Laugh louder."* **Do you still feel that way now (in August 2021)?**

That quote is still 100% true – you need to live BIG, you need to do things if you're scared. Do all the things sooner rather than later because no-one is guaranteed a future.

Do you feel more vulnerable in these COVID-19 times?

It was scary at the beginning, in 2020 when COVID started, and particularly having lung cancer. My clients are still scared so I coach them through it. I work really hard with my clients who are afraid of being in public, and possibly exposed, to get a deeper understanding of where the fear comes from and allow them to make a powerful decision that's not based on fear itself. It's been an interesting discussion which shows up a lot.

It's also very easy when you're a cancer patient to think every bump or cough or tickle or sensation means the cancer is back or you're having disease progression – everything is amplified and scary and it's very hard to live with that fear without letting it take over your life.

You don't get over it, you learn to manage it, and it all comes back to your mindset: What are you willing to freak out about? Understand and ask questions about why this feels scary: What does this bring up for you? What are you making it mean? Do you have proof this means anything? If you do, then it's fine to feel afraid. If you don't have proof, are you fine to make a choice about not feeling afraid? It's less about me giving advice, more about helping clients feel better and make powerful decisions for themselves so they can live with their own clarity and understanding of their mind, which brings more peace to a scary and stressful situation.

What is treatment for you now?

I'm still on targeted therapies, and I'm on the last one. This one will eventually fail and I'll be facing a trial or a traditional chemo treatment but paired with my current targeted therapy and possibly radiation because I have metastasized to my brain.

What are the day-to-day priorities for you now?

My priorities are: I do some form of self-care (meditation, self-massage, a dry brushing to stimulate my body in a different way), some form of receiving coaching from my coach or self-coaching to make sure my mind is where I want it to be – this could be reading a useful book or listening to a podcast to keep me thinking and learning and expanding. Physical movement, walking my dogs, doing yoga and I have added doing some cardio and strength training so I'm really existing in my body – this is the one body that I get so I'll do my best.

Any final comments?

I am so grateful for my initial coaching in 2019 that started me on the path of mindset, coaching and spirituality, which allowed me to develop the belief that I am not a victim of my cancer. I believe cancer happened FOR me, for my highest good, for my highest benefit. It's terminal, but it also gave me an incredible opportunity. If I hadn't been diagnosed, I wouldn't be where I am today, and I am incredibly grateful for how cancer changed my life.

3. "What a shame if this experience did not allow me to grow."

Ann-Kristin Dyrseth
Norway
14 August 2021

Although detected and treated early, Ann-Kristin Dyrseth's ovarian cancer has had various long-term mental and physical implications.

At the time of diagnosis in February 2017, Ann-Kristin was convinced her life in Norway would be over within two-and-a-half years which was the post-diagnosis life span of various family members who'd had cancer, including her father who'd passed away from brain cancer when she was a teenager. Now (in August 2021), Ann-Kristin has been cancer-free for four years, although the ramifications still remain.

When diagnosed with ovarian cancer, Ann-Kristin was told that she also had Lynch syndrome, a type of inherited cancer syndrome associated with a genetic predisposition to different cancer types. People like Ann-Kristin with Lynch syndrome have a significantly increased risk of developing future cancers, and it is this threat that continues to impact Ann-Kristin's daily life and long-term outlook. The future risk of cancer is a "cloud" that hangs over Ann-Kristin's life, which is compounded by both the limited medical knowledge around Lynch syndrome in Norway and other patients to talk with about their fears and experiences. For Ann-Kristin, cancer and Lynch syndrome go *"hand in hand"* and she knows it was her genetic Lynch syndrome that caused ovarian cancer at such a young age.

Ann-Kristin's treatment for stage 1A ovarian cancer involved surgery and chemotherapy, and included a rollercoaster of physical side effects and emotions at that time, from the hair loss and nausea linked to chemotherapy, the mental instability that comes from an uncertain future, being told her cancer was hereditary, and the highs felt four days into the second round of chemotherapy where the doctor shared the good news that her cancer hadn't spread, putting an end to the planned six rounds of chemotherapy. However, the Lynch syndrome and knowledge she has hereditary cancer remain.

One year after being declared cancer free, blood tests showed a number of irregularities which could have been gall or liver cancer – although cleared of these from further testing, life's "new normal" includes the fear that cancer will return. At the time, Ann-Kristin said to her husband: *"This will be my future now. Every time the blood tests show something, they will have to investigate if it's cancer again."* Ann-Kristin says: *"My feelings and thoughts about cancer change a bit as time goes by, but the deep fear that lies under the surface never changes."*

Ann-Kristin's attitude towards life is very different after cancer. Cancer taught her to set boundaries in various areas of her life. Plus, with three children, aged 10, 12, and 13, the fear now is that at least one will have the genetic mutation and develop cancer which Ann-Kristin says is a huge responsibility to bear:

"I worry more now about my kids, not just about daily life, but also who will inherit this after me. And how that will impact their life and their relationships. You know you can't protect your children from real life, from sickness.

Maybe I won't be able to see my children grow up. And I try to teach my children to be bold enough to always be yourself, that you can be caring towards others but also allowed to set boundaries."

Ann-Kristin continues:

"I was taught to please other people, and that I'm a selfish person if I set boundaries for myself. But as you grow older, it's impossible to please everyone. I was told from some that I had changed, I wasn't the same person after cancer. You have to change because I know so much more now. They say you'll live to 80 or 90 or 100 – I'm not sure that is my destiny given my increased risk of future cancer is said to be 80% because of Lynch syndrome, so I have to live my life for me and my children."

Although cancer-free, her emotional recovery was impacted by comments from outsiders regarding the short length of her cancer journey, with some questioning *"Was it really cancer?"* and contradicting the generally held belief that at least six months of chemotherapy is required for a diagnosis to really be cancer. *"I started to ask myself: Was I really sick because the chemo was stopped as the cancer hadn't spread, and you start to wonder – is this what everyone thinks?"*

During her cancer journey including the post-cancer recovery, Ann-Kristin was looking for inspiration and positive stories to draw from that would help her through the difficult moments, however motivation wasn't easy to find:

"When you say you have cancer, everyone knows someone who has died from cancer, but I was looking for stories of those who survived, the good stories, because it's the good stories you need to find and hear and to know about. I grew up thinking you either die from cancer or go back to work like you've never been sick – I didn't hear about the 'in-between' – all of the people in the middle who don't get their life completely back on track."

Undoubtedly, Ann-Kristin's life was *"in-between"* and, although cancer-free, there were still challenges to navigate. She thought that heading back to work was a way to both move on and avoid hitting rock bottom, but she realized that experiencing rock bottom was the starting point to building herself up again. Returning to work three days per week to avoid thinking about Lynch syndrome had the opposite effect, making her feel worse, so she began counselling.

With life forever altered due to the knowledge of living with Lynch syndrome and an increased risk of future cancer, Ann-Kristin spent time with a psychologist and undertook a number of short courses for cancer patients at The Montebello Centre in Norway. These helped her begin living her "new normal life" and provided the "keys" to cope with the mental uncertainty and fears that she has developed from cancer, particularly around survival and daily life, saying:

"It wasn't just one course that helped me, it was different parts of various courses that helped and made life easier mentally, helping me handle certain thoughts, family and life. I still use the keys given to me in these courses every day."

Convinced that her joy of life had been permanently affected, her psychologist asked which three emotions she would feel if life was the way she wanted it to be – her response was that she'd feel *"confident"*, *"safe"* and *"free."* These sessions helped her realize she couldn't go back to the person she was before cancer and there was now *"a new me"*, continuing:

"You cannot go back to who you were before cancer, there's been a growth. And maybe it is OK to never be on top again, but I have found an OK place that's close, a new kind of top, where I can function again. That's been a goal to work up to for me, and where I use the 'keys' from all the courses."

Family remains her priority, and the advice she would give to her children about life include:

"Chase your dreams. Do not care what others think of you. Go down a street in an unknown city singing and dancing like a happy crazy person – so glad I did that! Always be yourself, trust yourself, love yourself. Never doubt your worth. Use all your talents and skills – don't let people kill your motivation if you want to try and do something."

The personal growth obtained from the cancer journey remain with Ann-Kristin as she readjusts to daily life, raising her family and now working part-time:

"Going through cancer has really given me a reality check in people's true colors. Cancer changes you, but does that mean you change into a worse person? Cancer, fatigue, facing death makes you see real life more clearly, and you have to set boundaries for your own life. You grow and evolve as a human being. I think that is pretty awesome. What a shame if this experience did not allow me to grow."

4. "I've ALWAYS KIND OF LIVED IN THE MOMENT AND IT IS DEFINITELY TRUER NOW THAN IT HAS BEEN. IT HAS TO BE."

Lauren Hutchison
Ohio, USA
31 August 2021

When I first spoke with Lauren Hutchison in August 2021, our Zoom chat was interrupted by a bad internet connection whilst she was holidaying at another bucket list location. We rescheduled our call for one week later but, for Lauren, ticking off the items in her bucket list is a priority as she fights breast cancer which has metastasized to her brain and lungs.

Initially diagnosed in October 2019 with stage 3B breast cancer which has since progressed to stage 4, Lauren Hutchison, 40, of Columbus, Ohio, USA is someone who always lived life to the fullest, and is a cancer fighter who intends to continue living that way – as much as COVID-19 travel restrictions and lockdowns allowed at the time we spoke.

Although doctors didn't recommend surgery for Lauren's metastatic cancer, she initially endured 12 cycles of cytotoxic chemotherapy and is now on a maintenance routine of receiving hormone blockers every three weeks, essentially placing her in medically-induced menopause. A recent brain scan showed the existence of five new tumors which will require additional radiation and more chemotherapy.

The constant appointments and treatments have interrupted Lauren's plans to continue living a full life, however she functions as normally as her body allows which includes continuing her motivating and challenging role as a cyber security analyst for a bank, and spending as much time as possible with close friends and family.

In fact, prior to both COVID-19 and the cancer diagnosis, Lauren was out there living life to the absolute maximum. With a job that required travel for two weeks out of every month and a very active social life, Lauren crammed as much excitement into her life as was possible in her pre-cancer years:

"I've seen basically every major American city and many of the minor ones as well. I've seen all of the art museums across the country. I've dined in Michelin star restaurants. I essentially used my job as an opportunity to take extra time and explore the country alone and that was fantastic. I'd go out to karaoke. I had a circle of friends somewhere in the realm of 50 or 60 people. I'd throw frequent parties where we'd have board game nights and, earlier in my 20s, we'd have these fantastic parties where we had a traveling box of alcohol."

Living life to the fullest does leave a bittersweet feeling for Lauren, as she is aware that her enjoyment of life was a possible contributor to her cancer diagnosis at the age of 38:

"I had a very fun life. I have no children. I've been married for 20 years to the same partner, and I basically designed my life so that I would have as little responsibility as possible and be able to focus on things that were satisfying to me. And all those very same things that I enjoyed – drinking and eating

and not having children – are risk factors for my type of cancer. So essentially the cancer felt to me like an attack on my way of life."

After diagnosis, the lifestyle changed however the outlook didn't and Lauren is intent on remaining as positive as she can, reconnecting with family and friends as well as forming new friendships along the way. Lauren has renewed a previously strained relationship with her California-based parents, and extended the support network which includes her sister who has moved from California to be closer to Lauren in Ohio:

"My sister was living in California with my parents and she moved out to Ohio. I've been begging her to come for years. She finally moved so that she could spend some more time with me. Having that support network – from my spouse for 20 years, who takes care of everything day-to-day, from my sister, from my giant group of friends, and from people online, it has made the experience much less lonely."

Lauren continues:

"When I had my cancer diagnosis, I pulled together my friends and I asked for help. It's not something that I ever do. So that is another thing, a positive trait that cancer has gifted me. And those friends answered the call. And even though it's still my burden, people are interested in helping and, for me, that's the definition of love."

Lauren is not fond of being called "brave" or an "inspiration" by well individuals who don't know what else to say upon hearing of her situation, also acknowledging that some friendships can be fleeting:

"If you're being inspired just by the fact that I'm getting up and living my life like anyone else, it doesn't make sense to me. But the whole idea of being brave when you truly don't have a choice, that's pretty irksome. I tried hard to just understand that it's people who are well meaning, but a lot of it comes across as very disingenuous and certainly after two years of having dealt with

cancer, there are far fewer of those thoughts and prayers than there were at the onset of my cancer, and those same people who had come out after years of being dormant in my life, have gone back into dormancy as they understand that I'm still alive."

For well individuals who are unsure of how best to offer help or advice to cancer patients, Lauren believes providing assistance will always be appreciated:

"Ask how you can help. If you truly want to help, it's not the thoughts and the prayers, but bringing me dinner, doing my laundry. Think how other household tasks that are difficult to do, especially when you're trying to juggle a full-time job and a slew of doctors' appointments and scans all the time. So, ask to help would be a good one, and a second one is: "How do you feel?"

Well individuals could also go one step further by enquiring more about the patient's cancer and diagnosis:

"And another I would say is if you want to truly help a person with cancer, maybe learn more about their cancer. Because every cancer is different, so don't sit here and tell me you 'have a friend with breast cancer and she sniffed frankincense essential oils for a year and then her cancer was magically cured' when her cancer was stage one and mine is stage four. Certainly don't give any advice. If you want to learn more about the cancer, ask the person and they will tell you what is going on with their diagnosis, with their treatment, with their body."

Lauren also has faith that advancements in science and new treatments which provide additional reasons to maintain the fight without giving up hope, whilst also acknowledging it's her *"unnatural life"* consisting of a wave of medications that are keeping her alive. She encourages all cancer patients to keep fighting as new treatment trials are constantly underway that could prove life-changing:

"If I were to meet another person with cancer that was not as terminal as mine, I would tell that person to continue to fight because you have more of an opportunity to be in remission, which is the gold standard that everyone expects. But, if for some reason you're not able to become in remission and you simply must be metastatic for the rest of your life, then enjoy the time that you have because all of it from that point forward is unnatural. I now have an unnatural life. Life has been prolonged by medical advancements and technologies and if I stopped my treatments tomorrow my brain tumors would grow, and I'd probably cease to function within a year. There's always new treatments, there are always new drugs and just continue to fight because you don't know what advancements or what treatments might be just around the corner for you."

Although cancer treatments are evolving and becoming more advanced, the healthcare system in the USA does not cover the cost of mammograms for females under the age of 40. Lauren firmly believes having this procedure earlier than the on-set of symptoms may have detected her breast cancer sooner. She encourages women to advise medical authorities there is a family history of breast cancer, if necessary, in order to obtain an early mammogram, and reminds women who take birth control pills that the packaging states the pills can increase the risk of breast cancer.

As for the future, Lauren tries to squeeze every drop out of life, even amidst a life of regular scans and medical appointments, and a changed COVID-19 world with lockdowns and restricted travel*.

"I've always kind of lived in the moment and that is definitely truer now than it has been. It has to be. It really is a rollercoaster and you do have to be prepared to receive the worst news every three months, so I try not to plan too far ahead and I have to actively discourage other people around me from trying to make me plan in the future because I don't want to get my hopes up only to have something like COVID or additional cancers shut it all down."

For Lauren, there's no denying the impact that cancer has had on her life and overall outlook, or the way she lives her life moving forward, on her terms:

"It's my life and no one else can tell me how to live it. And I no longer have any kind of apologies about my own preferences and taking care of myself. So that has been tremendously positive for me."

* Due to COVID-19, ongoing travel restrictions were in place during 2020-2022.

5. "I HAVE THE ABILITY TO TALK ABOUT CANCER WITH PEOPLE AND ALMOST EMBRACE IT AS A PART OF LIFE NOW."

Dave Dubin
New Jersey, USA
21 August 2021

It was the first cancer diagnosis that led New Jersey-based, three-time cancer survivor Dave Dubin, 53, on the path to setting up his own Foundation – "AliveAndKickn" (www.aliveandkickn.org) – to raise awareness for people suffering from Lynch syndrome, a genetic mutation that can drastically increase the chances of a cancer diagnosis for individuals.

Now a two-time colon cancer survivor and kidney cancer survivor, Dave has a full life consisting of raising his three sons with his wife, working full-time in genetics, and promoting AliveAndKickn's mission to improve the lives of individuals and families affected by Lynch syndrome and associated cancers through research, education and screening.

As a public speaker, podcast presenter and difference-maker in the lives of people globally, the Foundation which Dave runs with his wife Robin has a Board of Directors as well as a Medical Advisory Board, corporate partners, donors and alliances. Launched in 2012, it's the first organization of its kind within the Lynch syndrome space.

Dave's cancer journey began in 1997, at age 29, when he was diagnosed with colon cancer following the development of recognisable symptoms. As with most 29-year-old males, Dave felt like he could do anything: as a ball player, soccer player, business owner, recently married, with a one-year-old son, and new house, Dave felt immortal. But, literally overnight the superhero mentality vanished with the diagnosis. His first bout of cancer was cured with surgery and six months of chemotherapy, and Dave returned to normal life working and raising his young family.

Following annual colonoscopies, Dave was diagnosed with colon cancer for the second time in 2007 which set off alarm bells amongst his doctors as, apart from a low iron count, Dave had no obvious symptoms and the colonoscopy one year prior was completely clear – this was when Lynch syndrome was also discovered, and proof of how quickly cancer can develop in those with the hereditary mutation. Following doctors' recommendations, Dave's annual checks included an upper endoscopy, which discovered a renal carcinoma on his right kidney that was easily removed by laparoscopic surgery.

Lynch syndrome's influence on these cancer diagnoses was instrumental in Dave's journey as a spokesperson for Lynch syndrome via the AliveAndKickn Foundation:

"Generally, we're not aware of the prevalence of Lynch syndrome, it's very common – it's the most common type of hereditary cancer that nobody talks about, and that's why we set up the Foundation. It felt like there was a need. I started getting involved in public speaking and getting profiled, and I became the face and the voice of Lynch syndrome."

Simply raising awareness of the availability of genetic testing helps individuals gain knowledge of their pre-determined 'panels', and the option of finding out this information is available both relatively easily and is surprisingly affordable.

"Genetics determine just about everything. There are panels of tests you can have done to identify various types of hereditary cancers and other things like cardiovascular issues. I would say to people: understand your family health history. If there's a family history of any issue, get a test to look for those things. You're putting together pieces. The panels have become inexpensive, and you get your results in a matter of days."

However, knowing one's predisposition to a certain type of cancer due to family history doesn't automatically mean they should live life with a carefree attitude to their health because of the higher probability that they will develop that cancer in the future. Living a healthy, well-balanced lifestyle can make a world of difference. Dave says:

"Lifestyle is always important. Will having a genetic predisposition determine if you'll get cancer? Probably. The question is 'when?' For example, I was 29 when I was diagnosed with my first colon cancer, I was always active, maintaining a good weight, good lifestyle – what was the factor that triggered my cancer at 29? We still haven't been able to figure out what causes the Lynch syndrome mutation to kick in and the body to stop fixing itself. Someone else could have the same mutation as me and not get cancer till much later on, or not at all. Taking care of yourself is always going to be the most important thing. There are certain lifestyles you should follow regardless of whether you have a genetic predisposition or otherwise."

Since fighting cancer three times following his first diagnosis at the age of 29, Dave is no stranger to the rollercoaster of emotions and "dark places" that cancer can send an individual. Working closely with cancer patients on a daily basis, Dave is well-versed at offering advice on how to work through the negative spaces and emotions triggered by cancer:

"You're going to have bad days, we all do. Cancer patients typically have more bad days than others. Tomorrow is another day and an opportunity. By having a conversation and being involved with organizations where you have someone to talk to, you feel significantly better. Some people feel better by discussing issues with others, other people feel better by internalising it – there is no playbook that says how you'll feel better. I've had the good fortune of having people around me who understand it and relate to me, and that's who I've stuck with. Not everyone will stick around – 'cancer' is a scary word, and people will head for the exits as soon as they hear about it. It's a roller-coaster. That's how life is. There are some people who will be there for you, and some who won't."

Dave continues by emphasising that remaining active and interested in various pursuits helped keep him focused through his periods as a cancer fighter:

"If finding something that makes you feel better, it's going to help you in the long run. For me, I played soccer through chemo. I felt miserable playing, but I'd rather feel miserable playing than sitting on the sidelines and doing nothing. For other people, it's painting or gardening – find what it is for you."

For now, Dave 's health-check regime consists of an annual colonoscopy and upper endoscopy as well as a yearly visit with a urologist. Every two years, he'll have a cystoscopy, mammogram, MRCP, and chest, pelvis and abdomen scan. Dave is also active in his three sons' medical lives, encouraging them to have genetic testing from the age of 18, given the family's predisposition to Lynch syndrome and genetic cancers. For the Dubin family, life with cancer and Lynch syndrome is dealt with head-on:

"I like to think that I and my family have been a good example of life with Lynch syndrome – that we discovered it, have been proactive about it since then, and we've shown you can live a very long, productive energetic life post-cancer. My sons have always seen me as a survivor and I like to think I've set the example of that – you can live post-cancer, and post multiple cancers."

Dealing with the medical profession and cancer patients on an almost-daily basis through his AliveandKickn foundational work while working full time in the field of genetics, Dave is grateful to have the opportunity to positively impact the lives of people internationally. Whilst many other cancers are well-promoted, the prevalence of Lynch syndrome and its influence on colon, gastric, urological and re-productive cancers in women remains very under-represented.

"I feel a tremendous value in what I and we as an organization bring to the table. If it wasn't for the need, we wouldn't be doing it. If we had the same type of penetration as other cancers, we wouldn't have started the organiza-tion. There was a need. There's still a need, that's why I feel a tremendous sense of fulfilment. We've increased awareness of genetic testing – some peo-ple test negative which is great and what you want."

As a co-founder of AliveAndKickn, Dave feels a great responsibility in his role as the unofficial global spokesperson and educator for Lynch syndrome and its impact on future cancers. The Foundation works closely with the medical industry to promote Lynch syndrome awareness and will continue to be a focus for Dave in the future:

"We've approached the Foundation like a business, which it is. Without ex-tending ourselves physically and economically, we've kept our risk low and return high. The long-term goal is growing the registry, that's really been a priority for the Foundation. By aggregating more data and bringing more people who have Lynch into the fold, hopefully before they have cancer, we can really put the research together that we can make a difference. That's the focal point. In addition to growing the advocacy space in terms of awareness. We

know the statistics and we're looking to prove those. I feel what's missing is the awareness on an international scope. The numbers are there. People just don't know about it. The whole awareness is still the biggest 'lack' right now."

Moving forward, Dave will continue in his role as an educator and major influencer in the Lynch syndrome space. It's work he's passionate about and he's truly making a difference within this field of research:

"I've had the good fortune to be able to merge my advocacy space and my professional space. When I go to conferences for work, I'm still talking to physicians and hospital staff about the benefits of testing and incorporating it into their practices. Then I can also have the advocacy conversation and talk to patients. I have the ability to talk about cancer with people and almost embrace it as a part of life now – we all have a certain amount of time on this earth."

Dave Dubin is living proof that the cancer journey can be instrumental in finding one's purpose in life. As an educator, influencer and advocator, Dave is making a positive difference in the lives of people globally and influencing the medical profession in a positive way.

If you'd like more information about Lynch syndrome and Dave Dubin's organization, visit www.aliveandkickn.org

6. "I'M NOT GOING TO ALLOW THIS THING TO GET THE BEST OF ME. I REALLY WON'T."

Vincent Keen
Shepperton, United Kingdom
18 September 2021

I was inspired by talking with testicular cancer fighter Vincent Keen, 58, of Shepperton, UK, because our chat reminded me of why I started Live Life Now Project, which was to live life as fully as possible, appreciate the time we have, and realize how lucky we are simply to be alive. This is how Vincent lives his life.

Chatting with Vincent was a reminder that we can survive and thrive in life without the *"doom monster"* that we carry around, regardless of our circumstances. His cancer journey started in 1989 at the age of 26 with his first diagnosis of testicular cancer. Since then, Vincent has fought cancer five times, conquering nine tumors over the course of 32 years through surgery, chemotherapy and radiation therapy. At present, he has three dormant tumors in his body which doctors describe as having *"gone to sleep"* – they live inside him, unchanged but observed.

A self-described colorful character, Vincent has lived on a boat on the Shepperton riverside for the past 16 years, an environment he believes calms his system and reduces overall stress on his body, which can only be good for keeping cancer at bay.

Having lived with cancer on and off for 32 years since that first testicular cancer diagnosis, Vincent has experienced the journey's many highs and lows: losing friends and family, finding, and sharing, cancer with the love of his life, cultivating a positive outlook, and understanding the 'games' cancer can play with a patient's mind.

One of the greatest treasures that cancer gave Vincent, was meeting his true love Yvette in 2008, and they became a couple for four years from 2010 when Yvette was diagnosed with breast cancer. Following a two-year hiatus, they renewed their relationship in 2016 when Yvette's diagnosis progressed to bone metastases. From this point, Vincent and Yvette continued to share their respective cancer journeys until Yvette passed away in July 2019.

Of his time with Yvette, Vincent says:

"So you got two people loving each other, sharing their lives with each other, and both had cancer which, in a funny way, it really is weird saying this, but it actually helped because you're both going through it, you're both going through all the highs and the lows and the ups and downs and everything else."

During their time together, Vincent was well aware of the clock ticking between them given their individual cancer fights. His love for Yvette was life-changing and very deep – her death impacted him enormously and taught him further lessons about life and cancer. Vincent truly believes *"the eyes don't lie"* and he could see the change in Yvette's outlook when she had started to give up on her fight once her cancer metastasized to her liver and brain, and her downward spiral toward the end happened. It was a look that Vincent had seen before in other cancer patients who had given up hope. Within two weeks, Yvette was gone.

Like most cancer patients, many relationships with family and friends are lost or forever changed because, as Vincent says, people are terrified of the word 'cancer', and Yvette's passing hit him hard:

"That was my soul partner, my soul mate, my best friend, my lover, my girlfriend and my partner. We could talk about anything to each other, and I don't have that anymore. That's gone. I don't have the ability to be able to speak as openly as I did with her because a lot of people run for the hills when they hear the word 'cancer'."

Of friends and family, Vincent has seen many come and go over the years:

"Some have gone, some have filtered in and out, and a few have stayed, but they stay at what I would call a safe distance. Most people just don't want to be anywhere near it. I would say: 'You can't catch it from us, you know. It's not like COVID. You're not going to catch anything.'"

Although these losses have had an impact, it's his positive attitude to life and a determined focus on his own well-being that have kept Vincent on track. Looking back over his life, Vincent believes cancer was the wake-up call he needed to change, which included emptying *"the rucksack"* containing the unnecessary items and emotions we carry around, that weigh us down in everyday life. For cancer patients, he firmly believes *"emptying their own rucksack of unnecessary baggage"* can only help with the cancer journey:

"You need to open that drawer, empty that rucksack that you're carrying around because there's a lot of weight in there that you are carrying unnecessarily. It's inhibiting your ability to be able to do your cancer. I emptied my rucksack a few years ago."

Vincent is also well-versed in the psychological games that cancer can play with patients, and explains his own methods for coping with the darker days:

"I believe that cancer loves negativity. It thrives on it. And there's too many people that have cancer that should actually try – I know it sounds like a bit of an oxymoron – but they should actually try to embrace it. You have to learn to live with it with your best endeavours. It wants to kill you. That's all it wants to do is kill you."

Vincent continues:

"Try not to think about it – don't ignore it, just try not to think about it. It's a bit of a difference, those two attitudes. I don't ignore it, I'm fully aware it's there and I'm fully aware that at some point, sooner or later, it will get me. The odds are stacked against me. I know that, but I intend to not sit in a tiny little cave and hide away and hibernate. I'm not that person. I'm the tough person. You go, 'Yeah, I'm here!' And that's how I deal with it. I'm not going to allow this thing to get the best of me. I really won't."

Vincent has attended cancer support groups over the years, having met cancer patients who let the cancer "doom monster" rule their lives, unable to break away from the doom and gloom aspects of cancer:

"A lot of cancer patients don't have the focus to take them away from the dark side. You gotta keep pulling yourself away day in, day out. It's a daily process. It's an hourly process. As I've said so many times, you've got to have that positive attitude. Imagine you're in a hot air balloon, and your negativity is heavy, and you're coming towards a building that you need to get over. And you had to change your attitude to be lighter so the balloon can go over the building. Are you prepared to do that? Try and lighten the load. Empty that rucksack that you're carrying around with you all day, you don't need it. Just because you've got cancer doesn't mean it's the end."

In his 32 years fighting cancer, Vincent has seen the statistics around cancer diagnoses rise at an alarming rate, and blames modern living for the increase:

"When you were younger, I remember most people either cycled or walked to work or got the local bus. People didn't use their cars, and most people didn't have a 2-hour journey to go to work and a 2-hour journey to come home from work, and work 9 or 10 hours a day. When they come home from work, they're stressed to the max. They don't learn to chill out, and they're just on this repetitive cycle every day. I think that's part of it, and I think stress is one of the precursors to getting cancer. I really do. I also think it's the food we eat. I think you've got to try and eat as cleanly as you can because that's only going to be good for you in the end."

Living in the moment is what works best for Vincent, who understands that cancer has forced him to accept that long-term planning is not an option:

"I'm afraid cancer has done this. I live for the moment now. I don't think you have much choice. One of the biggest problems is people plan to retire at 65 and have a lovely house and everything else. Well, you might not actually get to 65. Live now."

Moving forward, Vincent aims to maintain his positive outlook, keep that emotional rucksack as light as possible, and ensure the doom monster doesn't creep back in:

"You've got to look at all the positives. It's very easy to fall in that trap of feeling sorry for yourself. It's keeping above it. I used to say to Yvette: 'You've gone to the dark side, haven't you?' Come and join me on the light side. It's a nicer place to be. There's sunshine over here and you like sunshine.'"

∞ ∞ ∞ ∞ ∞

7. "There is nothing more gratifying in life than making a difference in people's lives and paying it forward."

Tom Hulsey
Texas, USA
5 October 2021

When endurance athlete Tom Hulsey visited his doctor on his 61st birthday in February 2015, he heard the words he didn't expect to hear: he had prostate cancer. And, like many men who feel embarrassed by this diagnosis, he shut down and shared the news only with immediate family. His closest reference point was his friend Bill who had recently died of the same cancer, and Tom was convinced and afraid that he'd share the same fate, which led him to a darker place emotionally and physically.

Adding to this *"shame"* and *"attack on his manhood"* was that Tom's friends and family always viewed him as "Mr Fit and Healthy", having competed in nine IRONMAN® triathlons up to this point, and leading an active lifestyle: eating well, not smoking or drinking, and regularly exercising. However, it was a simple gesture from a nurse in hospital following surgery to remove his prostate that set him on a different course, out of the darkness he felt from his diagnosis and surgery: she placed a blue band on his wrist which contained the words "ZERO – The End of Prostate Cancer."

ZERO (zerocancer.org) is the name of a US-based organisation with a mission to raise awareness of prostate cancer and help families impacted by prostate cancer, and also educate and advocate for research funding. Tom began a blog (tomhulsey.com) to share his cancer experience and also went to a ZERO Advocacy Summit in Washington, D.C., at which point he opened up about his prostate cancer diagnosis and journey and realized his feelings were the same as other men in the group.

Tom also confided in a close male friend who had experienced his own health issues, and who encouraged Tom to begin setting some goals to get beyond the difficult recovery days following surgery. Recalling the IRONMAN® mantra ("Anything is Possible") Tom shifted his mindset from one which was "fixed" to one which enabled "growth", which Tom now refers to as a *"winning mindset."*

In addition to the surgery, Tom believes it's this mindset shift that saved his life, and from which he set short, intermediate and long-term goals – the first long-term goals set were to compete in his tenth IRONMAN® and also walk his daughter down the aisle for her 2016 wedding – both of which he achieved.

Joining a support group and setting goals for himself allowed him to both focus and open up about his experience:

"It was the goal setting; and one of the pillars of my winning mindset is perseverance and persevering through those tough days and focusing on what the bigger picture was, and that's really what carried me through the darker days of my journey."

The ZERO ethos resonated with Tom as all funds raised are used directly to assist prostate cancer fighters and their families. As an advocate for the work that ZERO does to benefit prostate cancer patients, an underfunded area of cancer research, Tom believes that men's reluctance to talk about their cancer can inhibit recovery profoundly:

"For many men, it's the embarrassment and humiliation of having a cancer that impacts your manhood. Prostate cancer is terribly underfunded and misunderstood compared to other cancers because men don't talk about it. They do not engage because of the personal nature of the problem. I was there. Not talking about it definitely makes it worse because there's this stigma about it among a lot of men and that's why it's so hard to talk about it, but you've got to talk about it, it's so therapeutic. And as I learned as I've gone through my journey, hearing other men and their families talk about it, I can say: 'Hey, this is what I experienced and it's not so unusual.'"

For many men who 'shut down' and are unwilling to open up within a cancer-based support group environment, Tom advises talking to a close, trusted friend which can be an important alternative and starting point.

It's talking with prostate cancer patients from all walks of life that has become Tom's purpose in life. His career as a technology and cyber security consultant ended with his prostate cancer diagnosis at the age of 61. At 67 when we spoke (and still looking like a man in his 50's), Tom believes he has found his calling through his advocacy and coaching for cancer patients and those with heart-related issues as, previously in his life, Tom was also diagnosed with heart disease.

"After I got my diagnosis and I started doing the advocacy because this cancer diagnosis, and also I've had heart issues, has really helped me find my purpose in life. And that's my WHY. And now I've really dedicated myself to inspiring and helping others get through the challenges in their life, and I feel like I'm a subject matter expert when it comes to prostate cancer and heart disease."

Through his involvement with ZERO, Tom has most recently been working on a project for the US Government, called the Prostate Cancer Research Program, which evaluates research projects and applications specifically for prostate cancer – whilst the doctors and scientists on the project can discuss and evaluate the scientific and medical aspects of the research, Tom provides the perspective and voice of a cancer patient who has lived through the experience. It is meaningful and significant work.

Discussing mindset is also a passion of Tom's, and he refers to the dictionary definition of mindset as:

"'Mindset is a habitual or characteristic mental attitude that determines how you will interpret and respond to situations.' People talk a lot about mindset, but I like that dictionary definition as a starting point. And I talked about fixed and growth mindsets earlier – a growth mindset is the ability to learn, and it's not fixed and can change with effort, and failure is not a permanent option. And that's really kind of the definition of a growth mindset."

Following his tenth IRONMAN® and walking his daughter down the aisle, both completed 14 months after his surgery, Tom committed to his eleventh and final IRONMAN® 17 months after surgery, which was the World Championship in Kona, Hawaii – Tom used this as a platform to raise funds for ZERO as well as shine a light internationally on the importance of prostate cancer awareness.

Although he still exercises, Tom believes his IRONMAN® days are firmly behind him, preferring to focus on a simpler, healthier lifestyle and helping others. His daily mission continues to focus on working with cancer and heart disease patients to get through their darker days. In his 2021 book entitled *The Winning Mindset That Saved My Life (Second Edition)*, Tom applies the skills and mindset required to compete in an IRONMAN® to life's struggles. IRONMAN® is a metaphor for life and it taught him so much. Just like in life, there are many ups and downs in an IRONMAN® and how you deal with adversity defines you. IRONMAN® has been Tom's vehicle for several attributes, including determination, overcoming mental and physical obstacles, and healthy ideals. He needed all these in his health battles. Tom is so dedicated to assisting cancer patients that 100% of the net proceeds from the book will be donated to benefit medical research. Tom says:

"Now my goals are to positively impact one person at a time and what I'm doing through my advocacy and through the book that I recently authored – net proceeds from the book are going back to medical research so that's really what my goals are now, to help other people."

This includes encouraging men over the age of 50 (earlier if there's a family history) to have a simple, annual PSA test which could indicate that there are underlying prostate issues requiring further investigation. Referring to the current statistics and, particularly the impacts of COVID-19 on testing, Tom says:

"For most cancers the numbers are trending in the better direction right now but prostate cancer is trending in the wrong direction, and it used to be that a man was, according to the American Cancer Society, dying every 18 minutes but now it's one every 15 minutes. It's unfortunate that it's happening that way, but one of the things that's accelerated that or exacerbated it is COVID. A lot of men were not getting their health checks, they were putting that kind of stuff off. I'm actually mentoring a man right now who skipped last year because of COVID and now his cancer has progressed and he's not in great shape."

Tom's prostate cancer journey has led him to speak publicly about the issue, educate others on the importance of testing, lobby government relating to important prostate cancer issues, and assist patients with their journey. As Tom says:

"There is nothing more gratifying in life than making a difference in people's lives and paying it forward. What's your WHY? Mine is to inspire people to take action and be proactive with their health by sharing my lived experiences."

8. "All I heard were stories about death. I wanted to survive."

Margie Mobley
Tennessee, USA
23 October 2021

It was a will to live that helped Margie Mobley power through her private lung cancer battle in 2019 following confirmation of stage 3A adenocarcinoma in her lungs in late 2018 by her doctor. Talking with Margie, it was clear that she paved her own path through her cancer journey, keeping her battle as low key as possible, purely as a way to avoid negativity and focus on survival.

With no family history of lung cancer and never a smoker, Margie was reminded of her father's emphysema following periods of shortness of breath and panic attacks in 2018 when she approached her doctor and requested further investigation into her lungs, which led to the cancer diagnosis and the finding of a gene mutation that increased her risk of adenocarcinoma.

Alongside her husband of over 20 years and two daughters (now aged 19 and 31), Margie fought cancer privately, which included divulging her diagnosis to an exclusively small number of trusted co-workers at a meat packing company in Memphis, Tennessee. Her cancer was mostly contained in the lungs having also spread to lymph nodes in the area. A lobectomy was performed on the left upper lung in February 2019, followed by four rounds of chemotherapy and six weeks of daily radiation.

For Margie, the word 'cancer' had always meant a death sentence and was reminded of this 'fact' everywhere she turned: from cancer support groups, family members and colleagues. As a mother of two, Margie wanted to survive cancer – the constant stories about death from cancer forced her to retreat and fight her battle mostly in private, sharing her journey only with those who were supportive and able to keep her positive.

It wasn't until she'd heard stories of survival in online communities (particularly Instagram) of other cancer patients and survivors that she started to feel hopeful that this was something she could survive. Margie also discovered that a teacher at her daughter's school had fought a similar type of adenocarcinoma (although stage 3B, more advanced), and was inspired by the knowledge that she was still alive 17 years post-diagnosis. Margie finally found the hope and positivity she'd been searching for:

"Everywhere I turned soon after my diagnosis, I was reminded by people that cancer equalled death. They would talk about their grandmother or others they knew who died of cancer. I was looking for stories of survival. I wanted to hear about people who were living with cancer and living after cancer. All I heard were stories about death. I wanted to survive."

Also, her role as a mother of two daughters kept her going:

"As a mom with two daughters, one still in junior school, I knew I wasn't finished being a mom. That gave me a lot of inspiration to keep going and not give up fighting."

To help her through her cancer journey, Margie's strategy was to keep as busy as possible, continuing to work through her chemotherapy and radiation (with minimal days off for recovery), and keep her cancer private from work colleagues.

Margie acknowledged the importance of social media, online communities, and Instagram accounts like Live Life Now Project for those fighting cancer, particularly as they offer messages of hope from other cancer patients around the world:

"I have to say that it was Live Life Now Project and another cancer page on Instagram that helped me find the stories of hope and inspiration that I needed; to know there were people out there in the world who were fighting cancer, or had fought cancer, and were alive and still had a life after diagnosis. They weren't all stories about death."

Margie also believes that counselling should be part of every person's treatment program as many cancer patients navigate the psychological aspects of this journey alone. In hindsight, she wishes her doctors had prescribed some form of counselling to assist her through diagnosis and treatment, stating:

"Looking back, maybe I should have seen a counsellor privately to help me through, but I managed to work through it mostly on my own and with the support of my immediate family."

Margie also found walking, particularly in nature, helped her navigate the cancer journey, an exercise regime she continues today. She regards walking as the perfect natural medicine in her life, suggesting that the *"addictive"* qualities of long-distance walking, particularly after a long day at work, helped her reach a target of walking 100 miles in May 2021.

Now a cancer survivor, Margie was especially frightened by the potential impacts of COVID-19 on the lungs and kept a low profile during 2020 when the pandemic initially hit, mostly working from home and rarely venturing out unless it was to walk her beloved dog or visit the local store. As soon as vaccinations were approved, Margie was one of the first to be vaccinated by her doctor.

Margie now lives life on her own terms towards her five-year cancer-free milestone, however she still has quarterly scans to track the progress of smaller tumors on her lungs.

Having survived adenocarcinoma and dispelling her initial beliefs that 'cancer equals death', Margie fears cancer's return but knows that she has the internal skills and a strength gained from her previous journey to fight if it comes back.

For Margie, life is very much about living in the now, and says that cancer *"opened my eyes to the important things in my life"*, acknowledging that she now appreciates so much that she'd taken for granted before.

Margie's private strength and positive attitude shone clearly and brightly through our conversation.

9. "It has certainly changed me, I won't deny that."

Stuart Dovey
Shropshire, United Kingdom
29 October 2021

Talking with tonsillar cancer survivor Stuart Dovey from Shropshire, UK, it was very clear that he is someone who approaches life with both a practical and positive attitude, and was still able to learn and change from his cancer experience.

A routine dentist appointment in December 2019 for 51-year-old Stuart led to his diagnosis and subsequent treatment of tonsillar cancer. His dentist noticed a lump at the back of his throat and ordered him straight to his doctor, which was when his nine-month cancer journey began.

In the early stages of diagnosis, further investigation was required to determine if the cancer had spread from his tonsils to other parts of his body, which was a tense time for Stuart, however further scans and tests proved the cancer was contained within the main tonsillar site allowing for a relatively straightforward surgery and treatment program.

Luckily for Stuart, his car industry employer continued to pay 80% of his salary for the full nine months he was off work, so he could focus on surgery, treatment and recovery, which began in January 2020.

Realising he had a difficult road ahead, Stuart placed his faith in his medical team, whilst ensuring he remained strong for his family, particularly after breaking the news of his diagnosis to his 15-year-old daughter:

"A friend of mine lost her father to cancer when she was about 19 and her daughter lost her father when she was about 15, so I wanted to call her and see how I could talk to my daughter, because my daughter was 15 at the time. How am I going to break this to her? This is not going to be easy. I had that conversation and after that it was a case of: 'Well, OK I now know what I've got to do, I've got a piece of work to do. It's this long and I'm in their hands.' I've got my input, which is basically to support myself as best I can, keep myself in as good condition as possible and make sure my family are as happy and enjoy themselves as much as possible and are not stressed by this. So, I focused on that really."

Following removal of his tonsils via surgery, additional tests were required to prepare Stuart for weekly chemotherapy for six weeks, including CT scans, MRI scans and hearing tests (tonsillar cancer treatment can impact hearing). A couple of molars were also removed as the planned three weeks of daily radiation had the potential to impact jaw healing.

Knowing he'd be on a restricted diet for a period of time which would lead to considerable weight loss, Stuart spent time before chemotherapy and radiation working out and gaining weight. Given the neck area was the primary location for radiation treatment, thus limiting his ability to swallow food, Stuart also had a peg tube fitted into his abdomen which would allow him to feed himself through the tube with a pump.

The majority of Stuart's treatment regime took place just as COVID-19 was starting to hit globally in March 2020, and he believes the timing of his diagnosis in January 2020 made a difference in his recovery.

"I believe if I had been diagnosed a month later, they may not have been able to start my treatment. Whereas because I was already scheduled and I started on 2nd of March and we didn't lock down until 23rd of March, I'm fairly convinced that, because I was already in progress, they weren't going to stop me."

For Stuart, undergoing treatment during lockdown offered a few welcome benefits:

"The weather here in 2020 was exceptional and summer really started in March, so it was bright sunshine, beautiful weather. I got to sit out in my garden for months on end just relaxing. I was doing drawing and painting and I started learning German which I've carried on doing. And then when we locked down everything, with the schools closing and work closing, I got to spend that time with my wife and daughter as well, so we're all just chilling out together, having pretty much a wonderful six months. The weather couldn't have been better and COVID timed it really nicely for us to all get to spend the time together. I had a good experience really."

In the midst of his treatment period, Stuart vowed to keep as active as his energy levels would allow, starting slowly before fatigue set in:

"There's a little alleyway behind the row of houses that I live on. I used to go out there every morning, carrying my feeding pump which was hooked up to me and pumping food in. And the first day I did it, I managed about 500 steps and that was it."

The three weeks of daily radiation led to blistering on his neck, and the inside of his throat was impacted so badly that he struggled to swallow food. Plus, in the final days of his treatment program, Stuart was rushed to hospital following continual vomiting. Waving goodbye to his family from the ambulance, Stuart was unsure when he would see them again, if at all – due to COVID hospital restrictions at the time, family members were not allowed to visit him in hospital. This hospital visit coincided with the end of Stuart's treatment but, although chemotherapy and radiation were over, it would still be a few weeks before Stuart felt improvement and began gaining weight.

Whilst Stuart says he had an overall positive experience between surgery and treatment, he says the loss of taste was one of the worst side effects:

"That was something that affected me far more than anything else, because without a sense of taste everything is just textures, and they're not necessarily the textures you expect. It's like honey is actually like engine oil and there's nothing appetizing about it whatsoever. It is really surprisingly difficult to make yourself eat when you can't taste anything."

It took almost two months for Stuart's sense of taste to return and, even then, certain tastes came back before others:

"I can't think of a better way to describe it other than the tastes were 'far away'. It was recognizably that flavor, like bread or cheese, but it was just really faint, like just a hint of it, just on the horizon. They came back, but even now nothing tastes as much as it did before, that intensity has not returned. And I think that's partly because one of the permanent side effects is a loss of a lot of my saliva glands."

During my chat with Stuart, it was clear that his positive cancer journey was influenced by the various hospital staff with whom he bonded – he became emotional during the conversation when recalling the assistance and care he received, speaking of the hospital team with affection, admiration and total respect:

"I'm feeling tears come to my eyes because it's bringing back how I felt about those people at that time. I mean, I still do. It's bringing back the emotions

that I had because they were amazing people, they really were. I don't know how they do it because they must see so many negative outcomes, and yet they were unfailingly positive and warm. You felt loved. I got to meet 30 or 40 people I'd never met before, all of whom were warm, loving, compassionate, caring people: the doctors, the nurses, the oncologist. All of them, without exception, were just wonderful people and that was a major positive."

Stuart admits cancer altered his outlook on life for the better – he now finds treasures in the smallest of daily moments, which he realizes he didn't before.

"I've certainly come to the conclusion that taking pleasure in the really small things is a lot more important than anything else. Individual moments can just be really fabulous. There are times I'll be sitting in the kitchen and the sun's come down, and I'd see a little bird land on a plant and that gives me a lot more pleasure now than a couple of years ago – I probably wouldn't have noticed it, it would have just passed me by. Things like that or acts of kindness that you see out in the world every day that you probably don't notice. But then just little things you think, like 'How can I do things like that as well? What can I do to make people's lives better?' I think I'm probably a more loving person now as well. It has certainly changed me, I won't deny that."

In a world where technology dominates our lives as we are consumed with staring at our phone screens, Stuart tries to encourage the people around him to spend less time on trivial matters or meaningless activities, and focus on getting the most out of life, which can be cut short at any time:

"I try to encourage people to put your damn phone down, have a conversation, things like that. If you're sitting at home watching 'My 600 Pound Life' or reruns of 'Sex and the City', you're not adding anything to your life at all. Go out for a walk and just see if there's a plant you don't recognize or see one of your neighbors from down the street, stop and have a chat with them. Things like that actually make a difference to your life. Playing Candy Crush

or Sudoku for another 10 minutes, to me that's the same as saying: 'I've got too many days, I don't need them all. I'm gonna throw away a few.' It's just so pointless. I was like that before as well. There'd be days where me, my wife and my daughter would all be sitting there on our phones. And I look back on it and think 'Why would we do that?' But so many people do, don't they?"

For every cancer patient, the prospect of an early death can be very real. Stuart's treatment program was successful, however the topic of death did come up in our conversation, with Stuart stating that it was the impact on his family that concerned him more:

"If I die, I'm not going to know anything about it. It's not actually a major concern to me. How it affects my wife and my daughter is a major concern to me. I've got no plans on dying. I didn't actually have any sort of fear of dying for myself because being dead is not an event I'd be involved in, I'd be long gone by then. The dying itself well, that's transient stuff."

Moving forward, Stuart will continue to live his life to its fullest, appreciating every moment in the 'now' whilst still making plans, which include a family driving trip through Europe next year. His fitness levels have also returned – he's back at the gym regularly, and walking for up to two hours at a time:

"I don't live for the future, but I don't ignore the fact that the odds are very good that I will have one. The living I do is now. I don't live in the future and forget about now – that, to me, would be wasting the life I do have."

10. "REMEMBERING THE PAST AND MAKING PLANS FOR THE FUTURE ARE ALSO PART OF A HAPPY LIFE TODAY."

Dr. Marc Büdenbender
Switzerland
10 November 2021

D r. Marc Büdenbender has been a long-time supporter of Live Life Now Project, and someone I wanted to have involved in this part of the project. His responses to our survey questions always piqued my interest, and I felt his insights would be valuable to our followers and readers. When I messaged Marc in October 2021 asking if he'd like to be involved and interviewed for a longer story, he said he would but the neurological side effects of his permanent daily chemotherapy tablet were impacting his ability to speak.

So, we conducted our interview a little differently so he could still be included. I developed a list of questions for him and we conducted the interview as a written Q&A – Marc sent me his responses, and I then added more questions so he could elaborate on what he'd already written.

Below is the full Q&A. I'm very pleased Marc could be involved, he has so much to share that would benefit others.

Full name: Dr. Marc Büdenbender

Location: Aarau, Switzerland

Type of cancer: Adrenocortical carcinoma

Age when diagnosed: 45

How old are you now? If everything stays well, I will turn 50 next Spring (2023), and will be a survivor for five years and 15 years married. Reasons enough to celebrate a *"celebration of life"* event with my loved ones.

Treatment program: Three open stomach surgeries, overall 10 IV-chemo cycles (each a week in hospital with three kind of chemo infusions, permanent daily chemo tablet with Lysodren and substitution medicine (cortisone); genetic testing (twice Foundation One test and once holistic genetic testing by University of Heidelberg), staging every 3-4 months.

Occupation: PhD Economist, Former Head of Communication & Marketing, today Head of Marketing Projects and Senior Independent Advisor.

Did your outlook on life change upon diagnosis? If so, how?

No doubt, cancer has changed my life entirely with all the treatments, reoccurrence and side-effects of the permanent daily chemo tablet. I have to cope with neurological effects – such as problems with speaking, concentration and tiredness – an overall lack of physical performance. As a consequence, I had to change my job and stop with more intensive sports. I used to be a top manager and performance cross-country skier.

How does adrenocortical carcinoma impact your daily life? What limitations does it bring?

ACC (adrenocortical carcinoma) is very rare, aggressive and has a high risk of reoccurrence for ten years. With the high growth factor of my tumor cells, my risk is particularly high. I have to cope with this dismal outlook and with the side-effects of the permanent chemo tablet on top. This brings along many professional and private restrictions, as outlined above.

How is this outlook different from your outlook on life before diagnosis?

Since being diagnosed, I appreciate life with all its facets and much more. There's no time to waste. I try to accept the disease and live without regrets.

How important is a support network during the cancer journey?

My support network – with my wife, my loved ones, family/friends/colleagues and all the entire medical team, which is amazingly large – is extremely important to me. They give me mental support as well as the treatment options I require.

Who forms your support network? Did friendships change after your cancer diagnosis? If so, in what ways? Any reasons why this could be?

My private support network has really carried me. Relationships on all levels became much more intense.

So many people who are close are deeply empathetic with me. Only very few former friends have problems dealing with such a disease and contact with them has stopped.

How do you pick yourself up on 'down' days? Any specific strategies?

Talking with my lovely wife is core. Going out in nature for a walk with our small dog also helps. Other strategies include meeting/phoning with loved ones, going out for lunch/dinner, meditating, doing some physical exercise or playing the piano/listening to uplifting music.

How important is spirituality or a spiritual practice for yourself, or cancer patients generally? Is it an important component?

I am not religious or spiritual, rather more rational. However, I meditate regularly, do relaxing things (playing the piano, going out in nature) and get sufficient sleep. With my therapies, there's no day without a power nap after lunch.

What does a normal day look like for you?

Due to the cortisones, I wake up quite early and listen to music. Then I walk with our dog and have breakfast before doing some work (professional, gardening or at home). Lunch with my wife, an afternoon sleep, and coffee follows. In the evening I try to do some physical exercise (walking, muscle training), play the piano, be active on social media, have an early dinner and watch some TV. And taking in lots of medicine.

What are your day-to-day priorities now?

Most importantly to avoid any kind of stress. I try to live as consciously, physically and mentally active as possible, with positive social interactions.

Do you plan for the long term or live in the now?

Both! Living here and now is core. At the same time, remembering the past and making plans for the future are also part of a happy life today. I have many very concrete plans for my future and have already realized some.

How has COVID-19 impacted your life and cancer journey?

The COVID-related restrictions are surely not what I was looking for after such a rough period with so many interventions in life. Nonetheless, I am just happy to be here today. Coronavirus is relative compared to surviving cancer. This helps dealing with it.

What advice would you give to a well individual trying to cheer up someone who has cancer?

Cheering up with well-meant calls for happiness and motivation is the wrong approach. Asking good questions, being empathetic and listening does really support me.

In September 2019, your response to our survey question "The worst thing about cancer has been…" was: "*Not the fear of losing my life too early: I have few regrets and look back at a privileged life. It's the fear of how I would die.*" Just to follow on from this, do you have any thoughts on how we should/could come to terms with death (both cancer patients and well individuals). If a cancer prognosis is terminal, what advice would you give to someone about becoming comfortable with this inevitability?

To all I know, I am currently tumor-free against all odds while in 2019, I was called 'dead' with various liver metastases. In the meantime, I had many talks with my palliative care doctor, cancer psychologist and have planned a mainly mentally-focused rehab in a nice clinic in the Swiss Alps. Coping and digesting the prospect of potential death requires you to talk about it and reflect on yourself and the life you have lived. I also became a life-long member of Exit, which would give me the option for a physician-assisted suicide available in Switzerland, like in some other European countries.

∞ ∞ ∞ ∞ ∞

11. "The biggest happiness in my life comes from knowing I've been given a second chance."

Judy Hanger
Johannesburg, South Africa
14 February 2022

In the many years that I've been running Live Life Now Project, you'd be surprised how many cancer patients and survivors have said cancer was the best thing that ever happened to them. 56-year-old breast cancer survivor Judy Hanger is one of those people, believing that *"cancer saved my life."*

Before her breast cancer diagnosis at the age of 46, Judy would spend many nights sobbing on the floor of her bathroom (also called "The Crying Room") in the northern suburbs of Johannesburg, South Africa, pleading for help to change her life, feeling *"broken and worthless, and with no clue on how to even begin to fix myself."*

Up to that point, Judy had succumbed to the family disease of alcoholism, using alcohol to cover the psychological impacts of a directionless, troubled life. Still recovering from her marriage breakdown years earlier, Judy had the added burden of trying to cope with the deaths of her father and stepfather in the same year, causing her drinking to spiral further:

"I was in a very bad place in my life. I had five beautiful children but had never felt like I was enough, as well as feeling worthless for many years. With a broken marriage and losing my small business, I started drinking to numb the emotional pain that had become my constant companion. Drinking became the norm: if I was happy, I drank, if I was sad, I drank. Having a good day? I drank. I didn't have to feel any feelings. And I was smoking and going out a lot. Many nights I don't know how I got home alive. I'd go into 'The Crying Room' almost every night, literally crying and begging for help. I knew what I was doing was out of control and my life was going downhill, including my relationships with my children and family. I'd beg: 'Please help me to change my life. Do something.' To God, who I did believe in, but didn't believe was there for me. I didn't know how to stop drinking."

Two suicide attempts during this period also saw Judy hospitalized:

"My dark place was very dark, there was no light, only further judgement from people which pushed me even further and faster into the abyss of self-loathing and condemnation. These feelings were awful and a heavy burden to carry around every day, hating myself – drinking numbed all that for me."

Then, on 11 December 2012, Judy received the diagnosis that changed the course of her life: stage 3A breast cancer (estrogen receptive invasive ductal carcinoma). She had experienced a number of physical symptoms prior to the mammogram that led to the diagnosis. Two weeks later, Judy had a mastectomy, followed by eight rounds of chemotherapy, then daily radiation for almost four weeks. She was given the notorious chemotherapy treatment dubbed "the red devil", considered by oncologists and cancer patients to be the strongest and most aggressive available.

Judy barely left her bedroom during the eight months of treatment–chemotherapy and radiation wiped her out. Her mother and 12-year-old daughter looked after her, with her daughter also acting as Judy's *"guardian angel"* sleeping beside her, and offering the lifeline, support and comfort she needed to reach her goal: attending her elder daughter's wedding in October 2013. Judy found the will and motivation throughout treatment to remind herself:

"I am important, and I need to be at the wedding, it's my first daughter's wedding, and I wasn't going to miss it for anything. My hair had barely grown one centimetre and I was still so unwell, and I could hardly walk, but I knew I was going to be there no matter what. I walked her down the aisle. To have a goal and something to work towards and look forward to is immensely therapeutic and healing."

At the end of her treatment, Judy temporarily came face-to-face with alcohol again in the form of a celebratory champagne with her close friend Antoinette, who she met during chemotherapy, also being treated for metastatic breast cancer (Antoinette sadly passed away two years later, on 7 August 2015). They were celebrating the end of their cancer treatment together – Judy drank but the taste of alcohol made her feel so sick that she knew she was not going down the path of alcoholism again:

"We scheduled our last day of radiation together and we went out to lunch to celebrate – my body couldn't tolerate the alcohol at all. I used to enjoy alcohol so much. Again, one night I had two drinks with her, and the wheels came off. I realized this is what got me here in the first place – I wanted to change my life, and here I was drinking again. I decided that was it. So, I went to my first Alcoholics Anonymous meeting on 21 November 2013 and I've never looked back, not touched a drink since then. That was a huge turning point in my life."

These drastic life changes caused Judy to reflect on her past and, in particular, her friendships. Like many cancer patients, friendships also changed upon diagnosis. Her longest and closest friend (they dubbed themselves "Thelma and Louise") was scared by Judy's cancer and abandoned her at that time. However, Judy says she met the most amazing, life-enhancing people on her cancer journey. She remembers sitting in the waiting room at her first appointment with the oncologist when she was approached by an ovarian cancer patient, a stranger at the time, who gently touched Judy's arm and said: *"You're going to be alright."* The woman, named Lynette, had a positivity that was both moving and radiant – she and Judy became and remained friends until Lynette lost her cancer battle soon after.

Of her time amongst cancer patients during treatment, Judy says:

"There is an unspoken bond between cancer patients. Walking into the chemotherapy sessions, I felt the camaraderie between patients – there was no complaining, no moaning, it was very upbeat. Many days, I walked out of chemo feeling uplifted because I created beautiful connections with other people. Sitting in the chemo chair, I'd realize the patient sitting next to me was worse off than me, which made me feel less awful about my situation and more compassion for them. We supported each other. I enjoyed the fellowship amongst the others and creating a bond with these people that you otherwise wouldn't know."

Judy believes that people and friends come into one's life for a reason, but it's important to know when to let go:

"I don't believe anyone comes into your life by chance and, in hindsight, all the people who have been in my life were there to serve a role and a purpose at that particular time. I don't think you should hold onto friendships that have been there 10-15 years just for the sake of the longevity of it. You need to let go, which is hard."

Following treatment, Judy started a sales position selling gloves from a warehouse. The long days and alone time sitting in a warehouse surrounded by gloves led to her discovering her creative side: one day she picked up a pencil and started drawing, which has since evolved into a passion for painting, sewing and refurbishing furniture picked up from charity shops.

After an initial dream to create an organic healing balm for radiation didn't come to fruition because of all the red tape involved, Judy developed products named Tattoo Balm, Piercing Aftercare and two other organic based products used for tattooing. Her brand Tattoo Pro is now widely distributed from South Africa and makes Judy feel especially proud as *"it's something I've achieved and developed all on my own. Cancer can make us do great things we never thought were possible."*

Judy lives life in the moment, realising many of the things she used to worry about are totally irrelevant. Thoughts and insecurities around the opinions of others have been discarded and replaced with an ability to laugh at herself more, and *"not wasting one second of my life."* Even on the days where she wakes up tired and sore from her medication (Judy is on a 10-year chronic medication plan), she remains determined to make the most of the day:

"I get up and honestly don't rest a second. I don't want to get in bed at the end the day and think I didn't achieve anything. That has been the biggest change. Before, I was wishing my life away, I wasn't living, I was just passing time, hoping tomorrow would be better, hoping tomorrow I would find happiness, that tomorrow somebody would make me happy, or someone would tell me what to do or how to find happiness, and now I honestly feel the biggest happiness comes from knowing I've been given a second chance. If it's a beautiful day, I don't want to look back and think that I wasted it. I may not do the most strenuous things; I'll sit outside and paint. Being creative feeds my soul. I also find joy in the most arbitrary things – I'll see a bird bouncing

around or notice a person on the street smiling. I can now find joy in every-thing and anything."

Judy continues:

"I never thought I'd live to see grandchildren (Judy has two grandsons), *but they are now my biggest joys and inspiration to keep going. On my bad days I just need to see their little faces and I'm reminded all over again that I do matter, that my life is important and the impact that I have on people's lives is important. I am enough!"*

Life is now lived in 6-monthly increments: every six months, Judy has check-up scans and tests and, when she receives the all-clear again from the oncologist, says it feels like a "Get out of jail free card" – life can be lived to its fullest for another six months, until the scanning and testing cycle comes round again.

For other breast cancer patients, Judy has this valuable advice:

"There is so much post-breast cancer that us women have to come to terms with, especially if your body has been disfigured by a mastectomy. But it re-ally does make you realize that it's not about 'the physical' that makes us attractive, but really the light that shines from within – it's honestly the most empowering and amazing revelation anyone can have. I have also realized and embraced the fact that growing old is not a given but a privilege. I used to be so afraid of getting older."

Towards the end of our chat, Judy reflected further on life, saying:

"We're all broken, that's how the light gets in. No matter how big and black and scary that hole you're in looks, you feel you'll never get out, but you absolutely can! You're the one in control, you have the power to change your mindset and decide that you are going to fight. Your loved ones are as scared as you are, but they are your biggest cheerleaders and once you can get your head right and say to yourself and believe: 'I will not allow this to kill me, I'm gonna fight every inch of the way and I will never give up', your battle is

halfway fought. You are your own superhero and, believe me, just by getting your head right you can save yourself. I am the lucky one to have had cancer and to now be able to experience a new, fulfilling and very blessed life that I never thought was possible."

Post-cancer, Judy agrees that she sees life through different eyes:

"Everything is shinier and brighter. Believe me, the light that shines now for me after cancer is so beautiful and bright, and it sets my soul on fire. I am so blessed to have another chance at life and to really be able to live it with pure joy in my heart. Cancer does not define me and I am so proud of the person I have become."

12. "I KIND OF FELL INTO THE ASHES AND HAVE RISEN AGAIN."

Stef Gayhart
Maryland, USA
4 March 2022

It was the surprise diagnosis in August 2019 of a rare cancer that led Stef Gayhart of Baltimore, Maryland, USA to find her true self and discover her passion in life, which has been to help others in life-changing circumstances.

At the age of 37, Stef's stage 3-4 tongue cancer diagnosis was a shock as she didn't have any of the risk factors for this type of cancer, which is people with HPV (human papillomavirus) or men over 40 who have a history of drinking and smoking. Stef's symptoms began one month prior to the official diagnosis, however her dentist and a local Ear, Nose & Throat (ENT) doctor maintained she didn't have cancer. Unconvinced, Stef saw an ENT oncologist who confirmed the diagnosis via a CT scan.

Treatment was 18-hour surgery, during which half of Stef's tongue was removed and replaced with tissue from her arm to help rebuild the tongue, followed by sedation for 24 hours and two weeks' recovery time in hospital. Due to the operation and removal of the cancer, Stef was forced to relearn many of the basic skills that we all take for granted in everyday life such as breathing, crying, eating and talking:

"When I first came out of surgery, I had a feeding tube for about two weeks and then I started speech therapy, which was really frustrating at first, and learning how to eat again because basically half my tongue is just like a big slab of meat. The other half of my tongue had to learn how to take over and move for both halves. It took a couple of weeks, but I started to be able to eat more after learning how to move the food back at the same time I was learning how to talk. As the swelling went down my speech got a lot better. But then radiation came in and stole all that back away from me again and I've had more side effects from the radiation than I did from the surgery itself. I can't eat anything that's super spicy anymore. Even ketchup or pepper is too much for me some days. And I used to really like spicy food!"

When Stef returned home from hospital, she also needed to support her 6-year-old son Noah, whom she co-parents on a rotational basis with his father, as he struggled to adapt to his mom's appearance and situation. However, Stef found a creative way around the problem, which helped Noah relax:

"It took him a while to really open up after my diagnosis, and he wouldn't come near me when I came home from the hospital. He was scared, so we joked that I was like Frankenstein because he likes monsters so much, and because they had to take different parts of my body and move them somewhere else. Ever since then, he kind of saw it as cool and it's been fine."

The surgery and subsequent radiation treatment saw Stef lose around 30 pounds in weight, and she found radiation to be particularly tough, suffering extreme pain in the early stages of treatment which had to be managed with pain medication and feeling incredibly fatigued most of the time. Stef found the strength to keep going by focusing on Noah: unable to bear the thought of leaving her son without a mother was the motivation Stef needed to push through the difficult six-week radiation period through October and November 2019.

As is the case for many cancer patients, Stef also had to navigate her way around existing friendships and relationships which, in hindsight, she realizes had changed post-surgery and treatment:

"When I was first diagnosed, everybody was super supportive and wanted to be there. There's a term that a lot of people use called 'grief tourists', which is when people find out that you have this possibly deadly thing, and then all of a sudden everybody wants to be there. But when I was considered in remission, they all dropped off – once the hard part that was visible was over, they were gone. My parents are still very supportive, but the friends who were the 'Champions', who were there like my best friends, have completely dropped off."

Stef continues:

"It was heartbreaking at first and I was really upset about it because I just didn't get it, but now that I've had time to think about it, I've realized that our paths are just not meant to be crossing anymore or together anymore."

Professionally, Stef was a critical care nurse for almost ten years prior to cancer, although she came to the heartbreaking realization during radiation treatment that this part of her career couldn't continue: the long-term side effects of treatment as well as a pre-existing condition called Charcot-Marie-Tooth (a group of inherited disorders that cause nerve damage, mostly in the arms and legs) were going to impact her ability to lift, which is a nursing job requirement.

Given the new physical limitations, Stef re-evaluated every aspect of her life and developed an interest in the practice of mindfulness, living in the present moment and Buddhism (Pema Chodron is a favorite). She began reading books in these areas which she says improved her attitude and overall outlook on life, realizing the only thing we have control over in our lives is our thoughts:

"It really changed who I was because, before that, I was very anxious, always worried about everything and it's taken a long time. I still grieve my old self and certain things I could do, like with eating, drinking and talking, but I am happier now. I'm in a good spot now that I've gone through that process, and it's really changed me for the better."

Stef found support, comfort and new friendships within the cancer community as the shared experience of cancer helped form an immediate and understanding bond. She especially found a welcoming community at the Ulman Foundation, an organisation which provides support to young adults and their loved ones affected by cancer.

Deeply moved and influenced by the positive impacts of the work done by the Ulman Foundation team, Stef extended her involvement with the organization by becoming a GameChanger, attending monthly meetings and supporting other cancer patients for a short period of time, to help them cope with their cancer journey. Stef is also an advocate for National Coalition for Cancer Survivorship (NCCS) Cancer Policy & Advocacy Team (CPAT).

Of her work with the Ulman Foundation and CPAT, Stef says:

"It's definitely filling the void that I felt from having to give up bedside nursing. I still have that connection with people, and I can help people. It's really so fulfilling to give back to others in the community. Knowing that I can't directly take away their cancer but being able to be a support and showing that we do survive, and that there is life after cancer for some people and it can be beautiful, has been the best gift ever."

Whilst her bedside-based nursing career has ended, Stef's love of the profession remains: she is studying a Masters in Healthcare Innovation (completed in 2023) and occupies a Nurse Educator role in her local hospital. Stef has also brought her Mindfulness practice into the workplace: along with three fellow nurses, she has started a group called "Project Pause" which utilizes mindfulness concepts to assist with stress reduction and building resilience for hospital staff, including journaling, yoga classes and stopping to take 'mindful moments.'

In the two years since her diagnosis, Stef has changed almost every aspect of her life and outlook, believing that cancer improved her life:

"It has changed me more than anything ever could. I talk a lot about my 'Phoenix process' and how I kind of fell into the ashes and have risen again, and 'Stef 2.0' is stronger than she was before. But it took a lot. There's a lot of trauma that went with it. Before my diagnosis I was caught up in every little drama and the day-to-day things that everybody gets wrapped up in, and then this hit me. At first, I was very bitter. But then after a while I started to realize this could all end any moment, and I need to start looking at what I'm grateful for every day and be thankful for the moments I do have."

Stef is now focused on raising her son, completing her studies, and helping cancer patients both locally and internationally work through their journey. Classified as NED (no evidence of disease) in February 2020, Stef continues to have regular checks with her oncologist to monitor for any changes:

"I go to see my surgical oncologist every four months right now. He just does an exam and stopped doing scans. He said the evidence shows that we don't have to do them, and it's not really necessary at this point unless I start to have symptoms. So, we just kind of watch and wait, and treat the side effects as they come up."

Stef reflects on her changed attitude towards life and the positive impacts of cancer:

"I feel like I'm a more confident person. I feel like the growth that I went through that would have taken years was sped up, and I feel honored and grateful to have this second chance and this kind of wise view of the world because of what I went through. It's almost like seeing the world so much

brighter than it was. It's a gift. Cancer has been awful, there's no denying that. But it has also taught me many valuable lessons and given me a new appreciation for so many things. I feel like it has helped me wake up my true self."

13. "THERE'S A WHOLE LOT OF BEAUTIFUL LIFE STILL LYING IN FRONT OF YOU."

Kunwar Ujjwal Singh
Sultanpur, India
26 March 2022

Chatting with 22-year-old Kunwar Ujjwal Singh in his hometown of Sultanpur, India, it was clear that his experience as a teenage leukaemia patient influenced both his outlook and love for life. His bright, cheery, friendly and positive personality burst through the screen on Zoom – he's the type of person who instantly makes you smile.

An acute leukaemia diagnosis in 2016 at 17 years of age ended his plan to study engineering as he needed eight months of treatment. His initial doses of chemotherapy hit him very hard – Kunwar Ujjwal couldn't stand, nor get out of bed, was underweight and very weak. However, his family and friends stayed by his side and offered vital support – he admits he couldn't have gotten through this period alone.

Kunwar Ujjwal believes everything happens for a reason and this life-changing experience has shaped who he is today. His chemotherapy finished eight months later in August 2017, and he has since graduated from a Physics degree with Honours in August 2021. His plan is to teach Physics to students and continue undertaking research projects in this area. He firmly lives life in the present.

Below is a Q&A completed by Kunwar regarding his cancer journey and attitudes towards life.

Kunwar Ujjwal, how did being diagnosed at the age of 17 impact your teenage years?

It impacted me a lot. This disease hit me right at the age when I had started to grow as an adult and was about to explore all new aspects of life. But after diagnosis everything suddenly flipped. During the initial days, when I was admitted to hospital for having an abnormal increase in my white blood cells, no-one from my family told me that a bone marrow test would be performed (obviously having no idea what it was). After the bone marrow tests results confirmed I had leukaemia, still nobody told me anything. Everyone was like: *"It's nothing serious Sharad! Just some normal disease and it'll get cured by a simple procedure named Chemotherapy."* (PS: Sharad is my pet name).

At only 17 years of age, I knew nothing about cancer at all and I also had no access to the internet back then in December 2016. Still, I knew that chemotherapy is used for the treatment of cancer. Somehow, my mother succeeded in convincing me that I didn't have cancer because she didn't want me to panic. But after the first dose of chemotherapy, I was completely shattered. The horrendous side effects of the medicines made me so weak that I couldn't even hold myself upright. Amid all those frustrations and my quest to know what had actually struck me, I asked for my patient file from a nurse and the whole truth unraveled before my eyes, confirming my suspicion that I'd been diagnosed with cancer.

I was shocked and didn't know how to react. I felt numb, like some void was created inside me. How could I even react to this news? It was so difficult in that moment to even figure it out myself.

Coming from rural and suburban areas of India where "CANCER" was considered to be the end of your life because there's not much awareness about treatment and various other aspects, I felt the same at first, that this was my fate: the end. My dream of getting into prestigious colleges of India shattered before my eyes.

As a teenager at the time, it was too much to cope with: all the emotions and frustrations, getting high chemotherapy doses every week with horrific side effects and pain. The experience felt like the closest thing to hell during my first month of treatment.

You mentioned that your eight months of chemotherapy in 2017 was very difficult – what strategies did you use to keep going during that time? How did you get through it?

It was very hard at first. I had no idea what chemotherapy was going to do to my body and my mind. After the first two high doses of chemo, I was completely frustrated and almost gave up mentally. Not to mention the medicine which had to be given to me very, very slowly: one drop per minute. It's an experience that even words can't describe.

But my mother was there with me 24/7 and she became my saviour during that hard time. She gave me the strength to fight. I was discharged from the Isolation Ward after one month and then my whole family and relatives supported me a lot. Spending time with loved ones was the key to keeping my strength high.

One of the most severe and painful side effects I got from chemo was blood clotting in the urinary bladder, less than one month after being discharged from the isolation ward; this problem then persisted for about 40 days, which felt like hell at that time. The pain was so excruciating in my bladder that I couldn't urinate without support. I was also still having my chemo schedule at this time, and those 40 days were physically the most painful time for me.

After those devastating first two and a half months of treatment, I decided to come up with a whole new version of 'me' and, after that, every perception I'd had about life changed for me. My strategy was not to think about chemo even one bit. I regarded it as some normal treatment for me and told myself that these are the normal hurdles which will ultimately disappear. Looking back now, this seems to be unrealistic and stupid but it's what kept me going during that period.

It was the year 2017. Every time I came home from hospital after completing a chemo schedule, I kept myself busy doing other things like using my phone, watching TV, and exercising. One favourite pastime that kept me busy was watching cricket, especially Indian Premier League (IPL). Talking to friends on the phone and reading books also kept me well occupied.

Basically, I decided to forget about treatment and kept myself busy doing other things so that I could cope with all the trauma I was facing.

What advice would you give to another teenager who has been diagnosed with cancer?

The very first piece of advice I would give to a teenage patient is that there's a whole lot of beautiful life still lying in front of you – just don't give up, and keep your head held high. You became a warrior the day your treatment started, and warriors never bend their knees. Keep doing what makes you happy even during treatment. Develop any hobby of yours and spend time on that and, trust me, you will become a new upgraded version of yourself after treatment is over.

Based on your experience, what advice would you give to a 'well' individual trying to cheer up someone who has cancer?

I would say that the first thing someone should not do around a cancer patient is talk about the cancer. It demotivates and frustrates the patient. Try to talk about the patient's hobbies, throw some jokes around, narrate funny stories, and try to motivate him/her in the best possible way.

Also, if the patient likes doing something then do that thing along with them. Like my cousins used to watch cricket matches with me even when they weren't interested all that much in it. My father used to take a walk with me every evening and told me about various incidents and stories from his college life.

What was your experience like amongst medical staff and the hospital system in India with regards to your leukaemia?

There are a considerable number of hospitals (both private and public) here in India where top-class treatment for cancer is available. Fortunately, I was lucky enough to afford treatment in a private hospital, where I was admitted. Public hospitals generally have long waiting lists here in India. I wouldn't have been able to cope the way I did with my disease if I didn't have strong enough financial support. I consider myself very lucky regarding this. I can't imagine the pain and difficulties people with less financial support face while having treatment because cancer doesn't only affect the patient, it affects every person related to that patient. I have extra special respect for the people who are fighting out there with minimal resources available.

The medical staff and treatment system were well maintained in the private hospital. My doctor also motivated me every time she saw me which also gave me the courage to fight. All other medical staff were very friendly and helped me more than they are supposed to do as part of their job. Now when I visit my doctor for a check-up, she occasionally introduces me to other teenager patients and asks me to talk with them and do some counselling with them so that they can cope with their painful treatment.

How is the person you were before the leukaemia diagnosis different from the Kunwar Ujjwal today, in terms of your outlook on life?

There are a few perceptions about life which changed for me and some which became more fixed and constant. Leukaemia made me realize that the *"Life is uncertain"* dialogue is not confined to movies, TV shows and quotes only. It was the very first time that I had felt it myself, how life flips suddenly and sometimes even before you have time to react properly.

It made me sure that living in the present is what matters most in life. Yes, there are ambitions and future goals but that's all nothing if we aren't present at all. Every future goal and dream is achievable while living in the present and cherishing every moment you have.

This 'living in the present' quote I now live by changed me – after leukaemia, I'm always prepared mentally for any unexpected hurdles life has to throw at me. Because that's what life is about: you never ever know what's coming to you in the future. Being prepared for life's unexpected surprises is also a key to living happily in the present and tackle problems wisely.

That's what leukaemia changed in me: it gave me a vision, it taught me the strength of my family's love and support. It gave me a new vision towards life, and it made me value the present moment.

What are your day-to-day priorities now?

My only priority now is my studies. I don't think about cancer at all. Physics amazes me and that's what I do every day. Like I said, I keep living in the present and enjoying life along with my ambitions and goals and my family.

In August 2020, you wrote this response to one of our survey questions: *"Feeling low, tired of your life and hopeless? Congrats!!! You are about to learn the true essence of life."* **Could you expand on what you meant by this?**

Well, there were some complicated issues I was thinking of at that time. Everyone faces some very hard times at least once in their life. No-one can escape this truth. Those hard times can come in an unexpected way – in my case, it was cancer. Irrespective of what type of situation someone is facing at that time, it's universal that he or she is going to hit their lowest point. That's what I was saying with this quote. Everyone will face low points in their life and feel hopeless and, eventually, they'll understand what life really is about.

Even though you now have no evidence of disease, do you worry about reoccurrence? How do you deal with those thoughts?

I used to worry about reoccurrence a few years back. But I have changed my perception completely and I focus on other important things in my life now. I visit my doctor every three months for a regular check-up, and it keeps me relaxed that even if there is a chance of relapse then it can be detected and eradicated immediately. I do not let this idea of relapse hamper my other activities in life.

Lastly, I would like to add just one thing which I've said before: Life's unpredictability and uncertainty is the only truth. My chemotherapy completed in August 2017 but my "maintenance course" medicines continued until September 2019. Then, when everything was going well for me, I lost my father in October 2020 – that was the biggest setback for me in my whole life. Future's uncertainty hit me very hard this time and it was extremely difficult to come back from it. At this point in March 2022, it's been nearly one and a half years since my father left us, and we are still trying to recover from that. But this is what life is, and we must move on and create a better life for ourselves and our family. This is my life's motto, as it's been said that we either win or we learn. I never gave up before and I won't give up in the future, and that's what I want to say to all my fellow cancer patients across the world.

14. "I TRIED TO THINK OF CANCER AS A GREAT WAKE UP CALL TO HOW YOU CAN REALLY LIVE YOUR LIFE."

Tara Coyote
Hawaii, USA
30 April 2022

Hawaiian-based Tara Coyote spends much of her life around horses, thrives on a mixture of natural remedies, lives life amongst nature, is full of vigour, vibrant energy, and has both a luminous light and air of positivity that shined through the screen when we chatted via Zoom. And she also has stage 4 breast cancer.

Tara is someone who has defied the odds by ignoring the statistics and forging her own cancer recovery path, mostly resisting the use of conventional cancer treatments like chemotherapy to focus on alternative therapies and natural environments as part of her life with cancer. Talking with Tara through Zoom, one would never guess that she was both 52 years of age or someone with stage 4 breast cancer – she was the picture of health, happiness and vitality.

However, it took a meandering path of trial and error for Tara to reach this point.

Tara's decision to focus on mostly natural treatments was precipitated by a number of factors. She was 46 years old when diagnosed with stage 3 breast cancer in 2016, one year after witnessing her best friend die from acute myeloid leukaemia. Being a primary care giver to her close friend, Tara was impacted by seeing the devastating effects of conventional treatments and the toll they took on her friend's body.

In her own breast cancer fight, Tara's treatment program included a daily chemotherapy pill which her body couldn't handle due to internal sensitivities. Combined with negative experiences with the medical profession which she describes as *"pushy"*, Tara experimented with a variety of natural medicines and remedies, including a treatment regime in Mexico, until she found what worked best for her. She also worked closely with a team of naturopaths and acupuncturists as well as the well-known Doctor Veronique Desaulniers ("Doctor V") who authored the bestselling book *Heal Breast Cancer Naturally*.

Tara's aim has always been to stabilize her body, which now also includes vitamin and mineral infusions as part of her personalized treatment plan. Tara has been thriving on this regime of natural non-toxic treatments – an extremely well-researched program she has perfected through experimentation and discovering which remedies are more attuned to her body. She includes conventional monthly hormone blocking injections and occasional shots for her bones.

Tara admits that her individualized treatment plan wasn't supported by many within the medical profession and assembled her own team of advisors comprising oncologists and medical professionals who were also open to a natural repertoire of treatments to strengthen her immune system, which Tara felt was worn down by conventional medicines.

However, Tara undertook conventional treatment in 2019 when her cancer spread extensively through her body – to her lungs, liver, spine, adrenal glands and hip – and was referred to hospice care. This period followed nine months of chemotherapy, a time which also included emergency double hip surgery due to bone metastasis and was completed in February 2020.

Up to this point, Tara was living in Northern California and running a horse retreat centre and an Airbnb. Her health eventually improved and, following a number of stressful life events, she decided to move her company Wind Horse Sanctuary to Kaua'i, Hawaii where she has familial roots.

Wind Horse Sanctuary provides a retreat-like setting for patients or individuals looking to recover from a particularly difficult period or the stresses of everyday life, also incorporating the healing magic of Hawaii. Tara has an extensive background as a movement teacher and is a certified Equine Facilitated Learning instructor, life coach and grief specialist, providing a unique experience for her clients.

The calming and healing Hawaiian environment has impacted both Tara's emotional and physical well-being, as well as allowed her to reflect on her attitude towards life, particularly after losing so many loved ones to cancer:

"Cancer has been a blessing to help me really appreciate life, and it's definitely woken me up to a deep space of gratitude. I try to live in the present moment. So many of my close friends have died and my mom just died from cancer and it's like I've had a crazy amount of cancer in my life. I'm living with stage four cancer and I'm doing really well now, but I don't know how long I have to live, so that really makes me look at things like: who do I want to be around, what do I want to do, and really ups the ante for my own self-care because I know if I don't take good care of myself, my health could slide."

Tara's personalized roadmap through this journey is one which works for her, and she has so far defied the odds for a stage 4 breast cancer patient, prioritizing self-care:

"It's so important when you're going through cancer, whatever kind of cancer you have, to really give yourself that self-care and self-love and nurturing. There's a saying a dear friend of mine, a Hawaiian man says it's called 'Aloha Ma': it's 'self-reflective love' which was a big part of me tuning into my own healing when I wasn't doing well. I asked: 'How can I give myself the love that I'm needing?' because I'm really the only one responsible for it. I would encourage other cancer patients to take the time to find what truly nurtures them, not what somebody else tells them, but what nurtures their spirit."

Forging her own path has also found Tara seeking guidance from renowned thinkers and spiritualists such as Joe Dispenza and, particularly, Byron Katie to help question and reorganize her thought patterns. This process of self-enquiry allows Tara to "switch" her thoughts as a form of self-directed cognitive therapy to step out of any mental rut she may be in, improve the quality of her thoughts, clear her mind, and provide a positive healing force. For Tara, the process was challenging in the beginning however, with effort, she was able to incorporate these techniques into her daily life, and maintain a health-centered, healing-based mindset:

"I really believe in the infinite power of healing. Yes, I'm living with stage four cancer, but I don't think of myself as 'sick' and I never have. When I was not doing well three years ago, I thought of myself as sick, but I see myself as healthy. And I wake up with the thought every day that 'I am healthy, I'm healing' rather than 'Oh my God. When am I going to die?' It's challenging though, I have to really work at it because that fear is there too, I'll acknowledge that."

Taking on board the valuable advice from a dear friend who said: *"Don't let cancer be your story,"* Tara believes that *"Cancer is part of my story, but it's not MY story. It's not everything about me. A lot of times people are diagnosed and it's so easy to fall into that victim state of mind and have cancer just rule your life like: 'I can't go do this because I have cancer, now my life is ruined.' I tried to think of cancer as a great wake up call to how you can really live your life."*

This extensive inner work has placed Tara in tune with her emotions and the games that cancer can play with the patient's mind, advising fellow cancer patients:

"To really pay attention to your emotions. Whatever fears might come up: anger, sadness – get the message behind the emotions and attend to whatever fear and terror that they might be associating with their cancer. Get support. Find a therapist. Try to switch your thoughts around and see beyond the limitations."

Tara continues:

"Living with cancer is an incredible mindfuck because there's so much fear about it. Cancer is equated with death in our culture and because we're a death-phobic culture, if people hear you have cancer, they automatically assume you're on your way out."

As with many cancer patients, Tara's friendships and relationships have changed, and she agrees that it's important to maintain a healthy support network whilst also purifying one's life of toxic relationships:

"It's really important to be around people that nurture and support you and love you for who you are. There were definitely some relationships, and it was very painful to let go of the relationship, but people that felt toxic, and I've lost some relationships over my choices. It's sad, but it's important for each of us to honor our own individual path, because we're all unique and not everybody is going to love you and that's OK. There are the people who will love and adore you, and those are the ones that you should surround yourself with."

Living in Hawaii has undoubtedly had a positive impact on Tara's attitude and perspective on life, believing the natural surroundings and calming influence of the island have benefited her health enormously:

"I feel like nature is extremely healing and specifically in Hawaii, there's a lot of 'Mana' which is a Hawaiian word for 'spirit's healing power.' That's very tangible – the nature is very alive, very green. It's always raining and then the sun comes out and the birds are chirping so I feel like nature and being around animals is incredibly healing. Just being in the quiet. And because we human beings can get so busy in our minds and what we do and it can just be overwhelming, and to go into nature and be near a tree, and listen to the roosters and the wind, it can really calm down the nervous system."

Horses have played a big role in Tara's life, and they are used extensively to assist with the healing of clients who visit Tara for coaching sessions. Equine Facilitated Learning incorporates the energy of horses to help people find their true inner wisdom and bring balance into their lives. During our chat, I was curious to learn more about the healing nature of horses, and Tara says:

"Horses have huge hearts. We're taught in our Western civilization about how powerful the mind is, but the heart, and the energetics of the heart, is much more powerful. The reason why horses are so healing is because they have these huge hearts. Their energetic presence is so strong and they're very calming to be around. They're extremely reflective. If a client is suppressing anger or grief, the horses' presence just sort of pulls those stuck emotions out of them."

Tara believes that her passion around running Wind Horse Sanctuary and having a work schedule are necessary for her healing, keeping her busy and focused, with her animals forming an important part of her support network:

"I feel like my animals honestly are a big part of why I'm doing well: my horses, my dog and I have 3 cats – I feel like they hold a lot of energetic support for me. The act of just tending to the horses and scooping their manure or feeding them is incredibly healing. Because I have so many animals, I can't just not feed them for days, so I would say my life is pretty much built around my animals and the land. Besides that, I'll have clients and I'll do interviews and I'm working on different books so it kind of varies each day, but there's a lot to do with my animals, which is great. I love it."

Setting realistic and achievable goals is another aspect of life that Tara finds beneficial, whether it be arranging a trip with friends on another of the Hawaiian Islands, or to see a live band:

"It helps me to have something to look forward to, like a reward. I believe it's always important to have something to look forward to because sometimes it can be really tough. And I try to fit a little bit of joy and relaxation into every day."

It seems that Tara has now found her "sweet spot" in life, having published her own memoir, been featured in the books of other authors, produced an award-winning environmental 10-minute short film (*Honor The Earth*), is working on her second book, and being active on social media. She documents aspects of her late-stage breast cancer journey on her website and You Tube channel, providing an enormous amount of support and an active online community for other breast cancer fighters around the world.

It was such a joy and inspiration to have this chat with Tara Coyote, someone who vehemently lives life on her terms whilst also shining a light on the world.

∞ ∞ ∞ ∞ ∞

15. "Don't wait to do things in a year. If you have the chance to do it now, then do it now."

Mari Carmen
Barcelona, Spain
1 May 2022

Talking with breast cancer survivor Mari Carmen from Barcelona in Spain, it's clear that she is a different person post-cancer than she was before her stage 2 breast cancer diagnosis at the age of 42 in February 2018.

Before cancer, Mari says she floated through life like the rest of us, complaining about trivial matters, working hard as an Administration Assistant for an IT company, and constantly rushing to get things done. However, the breast cancer diagnosis came as a surprise as there was no history of breast cancer in her family, and her lifestyle comprised of eating healthily, and not drinking or smoking.

However, that breast cancer diagnosis in 2018 changed everything about Mari's outlook on life and how she lives each day. Her treatment program consisted of a total right breast mastectomy and reconstruction, and 16 rounds of chemotherapy, 25 radiotherapy sessions, one year of immunotherapy and targeted therapy injections, and a five-year program of hormone therapy. Mari has an annual MRI scan to check for any signs of reoccurrence. She is now in remission with no evidence of disease, enjoying life in the present. There's no question that she is a changed person, appreciating every moment in her life whilst also giving back to the cancer community in various ways.

In this Q&A, Mari talks about her life before and after cancer, as well as various tools she used to help get her through treatment.

Mari, what was your outlook on life before diagnosis, and how is it different now?

Before cancer, I was a passenger in life, thinking about problems from day to day, planning holidays, going to concerts with my friends, and working hard every day with little time for myself. I was always in a hurry.

I viewed my life without perspective, traveling through with no idea or plans for the long term. I was just planning and doing, not thinking that everything could change in one minute. When you are told you have cancer, your life changes in that moment. That day, I entered the hospital as Mari Carmen, then I was told I had cancer, and I left the hospital a different person – I felt I was suddenly inside a storm.

Now, I always think how lucky I am because I wasn't supposed to be here. For example, at a recent concert (Bon Jovi in Madrid), I was thinking *"Thank you"* to my oncologist and all the cancer researchers for their work over many years – their work kept me alive so I could enjoy this moment because I felt like I wasn't meant to be there enjoying myself. Whenever I'm experiencing something now, it's always at the back of my mind that there was a chance I wouldn't have made it here to have this experience. I'm thankful for everything.

I always think that I made an exchange: I exchanged my right breast for years of life. Many people are not as lucky. We all wake up in the morning and don't know what's going to happen that day – someone who wakes up today is going to have a stroke or a heart attack or a car accident, and they won't have the chance to make this exchange like I did.

What changes have you made to your life since diagnosis?

I decided to do at least one thing every month that I had never done before, like going to the opera, to a new place, starting a course, learning something new, seeing exhibitions. I try to use my time in worthwhile ways, trying to have experiences and make memories.

I'm braver now than I was, and I don't complain about silly things anymore. If someone doesn't like me, it's no longer a problem for me. If I am invited to a party that I don't want to attend, I don't go. I was always the person who didn't have the bravery to say *"No."* Now I do, and I don't feel bad for it. I think it's important to be able to say *"No"* and not feel bad about it.

My work colleagues have told me that I used to be like the 'mama' at the company because I was always looking out for everyone, making them feel good, welcoming them, trying to help everyone as much as possible – I've stopped that behaviour. I only take care of people I work closely with who are on my side. It might seem selfish, but I don't waste time on people who don't show the same care for me.

Since diagnosis, I have also changed my dress style. Because I love rock and roll music, I always wore black and grey clothes and rock band t-shirts (AC/DC, U2). Now, my clothes are more colorful, and I wear dresses and skirts, which I didn't wear before, as I was always in jeans.

When you have cancer and have to wear hats, scarves or bandanas on your head, you need these accessories. When I started to feel well, I continued wearing a lot of scarves and earrings, most of them in big sizes and colors. Someone who hasn't seen me for five years wouldn't recognise me now.

What are your day to day priorities now?

To be mentally, physically and psychologically healthy, for both me and my family. The most important thing is to take care of yourself, in any way that you can – exercising, eating healthily, and trying to remove as much stress as possible. There's nothing more important than being healthy.

I also try to enjoy the moment, and not plan too far into the long term – I focus on the short and medium term, just a few months ahead. This is a lesson I learned from cancer and a lot of us learned from the COVID pandemic – we live in a very unstable world. I live in the short-to-medium term, because you could have the most wonderful and amazing plans for the longer term, but you could be 'slapped' by cancer, which wasn't in the script. I will plan and look forward to holidays a few months ahead, but not longer, because life has taught me that anything can change in a minute.

How else would you say your life has changed since diagnosis?

I feel brave, and I feel part of the cancer community and the survivor community. As much as I can, I try to help people who are in the same situation I was in. I'm part of a 'patient's association' where I help other patients with advice and information based on my cancer experience. I also donate money to cancer research and provide support to patients during their treatment – nobody understands the cancer experience as much as a cancer patient who has been through it, so I try to help as much as I can.

I also collaborate with the Juegaterapia Foundation which makes "Pelones" dolls – they sell these dolls to raise money to improve the hospital stay for cancer patients, especially children, and I try to promote Pelones sales to help them raise money for the Foundation. For example, they might change the hospital surroundings for kids to make it look like they're on a special trip into space. My sister gave me my first doll as a gift when I lost my hair. They come with a scarf which is usually designed by a famous Latino/Spanish person like Shakira, Ricky Martin or Rossy de Palma. My sister and I sew the doll's clothes, and I opened an Instagram account related to the dolls when I was on sick leave with plenty of free time. For me, the most beautiful thing about this initiative is that many sick children message to ask me to make dresses for their dolls and give their dolls a name and ask if our dolls can be "cousins" with each other.

I've also stopped complaining about trivial everyday things and can't understand when people do, because I feel, for example: *"Is your biggest problem that your boss doesn't pay you enough money? Is this your biggest problem? Do you know that someone somewhere today has been told that they have cancer, or their family member has cancer?"* This is why I can't tolerate people who complain about trivial matters in daily life. Another recent example is that my football team lost a championship, and they were very upset. I told other fans that the team will try again next year – some people don't have that chance to try again. I focus on important matters, which has been the most significant change since I was diagnosed. I've changed the way I see everything.

Like everyone, I was going through life mainly in a hurry, feeling I was short on time. When I was on sick leave, going to hospital appointments and chemotherapy, I was able to stop and watch other people, hear them complaining, always rushing and in a hurry running errands without stopping, and I realized I was the same before cancer. Cancer gave me the chance to stop and think about how I lived my life before the diagnosis, and I don't want to go back to living that way.

How important was a support network during your cancer journey?

It was very important for me. I was in a breast cancer patient group as I was trying to learn as much as possible from patients who were further along in their journey than me. They are the people that can give you tips, and I was able to see that I wasn't the only one with cancer, not the first or the last, and when you see another person who has gone through the same experience and you can see they look and feel good, it's amazing. The group was important because, as a patient, you think what you're going through is only happening to you, and you realize that others are going through a similar ordeal. Further along in my treatment and journey, I was then able to give support to new patients and could see myself reflected in them as I had been through a similar experience – I could help each of them in the same way that others before me, helped me in the beginning.

It's also amazing how the internet can connect you with others who can help you by sharing their experience, which is so valuable. There are people with blogs and Instagram accounts who can provide information about their treatment, which was gold for me. They also inspired me because I could see they survived their treatment and it made me believe I would too, even when it was difficult.

I also had family, friends, work colleagues, and social media contacts I met in person – I had many people around me who helped a lot. I know people who are not as lucky as me to have this support and I know it's difficult for them because it makes a difference when you have someone to help you or cook for you. When I told people I was ill, I had plenty of offers from family and friends for help – I was very lucky.

What strategies helped you through treatment?

I had good and bad days, everything. I had counselling by a psycho-oncologist who told me in the beginning that, when you have cancer, every thought that comes into your mind relates to the illness. Your fears appear every moment of the day, like when you're shopping, and then you feel bad. To work around this, my psycho-oncologist told me to dedicate 10-15 minutes every day to think about the illness and these negative thoughts – focus on them only during this time, and then try not to think of these fears and things again during the day. If you are worrying and thinking every single moment, you can't relax. Once you've done your allocated time, then you can tell yourself that you are free to get on with the day. This helped me a lot.

I also tried to be distracted and active by doing exercise, eating well, and having things to do apart from going to the hospital or treatment appointments. Try to live as normal a life, maybe you can go to the cinema, go for a walk – because you are ill, it doesn't mean you have to stay at home. We have this idea that a cancer patient is spending all day in bed crying, and this is not the cancer patient today. If it wasn't for the hair loss, maybe others wouldn't notice you have cancer because you might be able to many normal things. A few days after chemotherapy I felt tired, but usually I felt ok. I was also in a very positive state of mind.

Losing my hair through chemotherapy wasn't a problem for me. People warned me about losing my hair as though it's going to be the worst thing, but for me it wasn't the worst thing at all – the way I felt during my chemotherapy was worse for me, the symptoms and the side effects that I felt, not the 'external' ones that can be seen like losing hair or losing weight, but the ones that only the patient knows, like peripheral neuropathy, loss of taste and smell, and 'chemo brain.' We live in a society where image is the most important thing, which is why so much emphasis is placed on losing hair. This was something I never understood: measuring the quality of a cancer patient's life by the state of their hair. It never made sense to me. And then, when your hair starts to grow back, people think you are totally recovered, which isn't true.

I read all I could related to my cancer, and I became an expert in HER 2-positive breast cancer. I wanted to know everything so I could understand the doctors' reports. It helped me to know the 'enemy', which then helped me to 'forgive' my cancer because I realized I couldn't do anything to avoid it – I understood the cancer cells multiplied as a survival instinct, so I was able to forgive my cancer by saying: *"I understand, and I forgive you."*

How did you pick yourself up on down days? What advice do you give to people having a bad day?

There are two things I think when I have a bad day: there is something even worse than having cancer, which is to have cancer without knowing you have cancer. Once you know you have cancer, all the machinery helps you to survive. And if I have a bad day, I always think someone somewhere today has been told they have cancer – this is the worst thing you can hear. I don't care if you've had a bad day in the office, at your job, in the traffic, with your children, whatever – if you haven't been told today you have cancer, you have had a good day, the best day you can imagine. Nothing compares to hearing these three words: *"You have cancer."* If you don't hear these three words in any day of your life, you have been lucky.

When people asked about side effects, they only wanted to hear the bad ones, like that I was tired. I always talked about the most important one, and the only one that matters, which was that the best side effect of the treatment was to be alive! This attitude helped me when I had a bad day. When told you have cancer, you simply have to go through the process because there's no other option.

Try to enjoy the process where you can – there are a lot of things along the way that you will remember with a smile, like your last chemo day; you will remember this with a smile because it means finishing part of the treatment – there are many good things along the way. Try to celebrate them in some way, try to see the good in these situations. Mark the day somehow: buy yourself a lipstick, a bag, an earring – mark the occasion. Give yourself presents to remember the good things that happen during treatment.

I don't have a lot of bad days because every day I wake up I try to say thank you for another day because, apart from my experience, I think COVID has taught us that life can change in a minute so try not to worry about simple things.

I would also listen to music, watch funny movies, TV series – the usual activities.

What advice would you give to a 'well' individual trying to cheer up someone who has cancer?

Just ask what they need because it depends on the moment, as they will need different things at different times. Sometimes all they need is for you to be by their side without talking, just sitting there. Respect their time because when ill, the patient is always asked *"Are you feeling better?"* and it doesn't get better so quickly, especially when going through chemotherapy.

Try to distract them by, for example, going to the cinema. It's also very important to treat them in a normal way and, if the person is in a good mood, try to make fun of the situation, make them laugh, because if they can make fun of the situation, they are almost there – for example, if a patient can make light of their hair loss, it helps them psychologically.

Mari, it's been great talking to you. Anything else you'd like to add?

Don't wait to do things in a year. If you have the chance to do it now, then do it now because you don't know where you'll be in a year. Like, don't wait for a specific occasion to wear a nice dress for the first time, wear it now. Don't wait.

16. "I WAS LIVING FROM FEAR. BUT WHEN YOU LIVE FROM LOVE, EVERYTHING CHANGES."

Paola Benitez
Colombia, South America
20 June 2022

For Colombia-based Paola Benitez, it took three separate and independent cancer diagnoses within two years to learn that she needed to heal her life and listen to her body. Through this painful and difficult process, she made the decision to live life from a place of love and not fear which guided Paola through her cancer journey and how she lives her life today.

In December 2018, at the age of 38, Paola was first diagnosed with stage 1 breast cancer. While in surgery to remove the tumor, doctors discovered unusual tissue which was also removed and biopsied, revealing she'd also had Non-Hodgkins lymphoma. Then, in December 2019, Paola was diagnosed with thyroid cancer which was treated via surgery to remove the tumor one month later.

This two-year whirlwind of three diagnoses, multiple operations and various chemotherapy and radiotherapy sessions forced Paola to look at how she was living her life in such a way that caused her body to become afflicted with separate cancers. Paola's doctors undertook extensive genetic and DNA testing to understand if there were any family links to her various cancers yet found there were none, confirming the suspicion that the stress in Paola's personal and professional lives played a key role.

A major source of stress for Paola prior to the first cancer diagnosis related to her bullying harassment claim against a boss at work. Paola was aware that her role as a Political Scientist in a Development Program within this International Corporate Agency at the time of her diagnosis caused stress on both her mind and body, leaving her tired, weak and with low self-esteem. Paola thought she was coping with her stress in a healthy way, but later realized her strategies weren't working, crying often and working overtime on weeknights and weekends to 'protect' her job.

At the same time, Paola recognized that her three-year relationship with her boyfriend was another source of stress. He had lost his job and Paola felt she needed to remain in her traumatizing work situation to support them and their living arrangement, so quitting her job wasn't an option.

The stress at home and work became too much, and Paola recognizes the negative effects caused by these factors played a key role in triggering her cancers, which she believes was the wake-up call she needed to address the stress in her life.

Doctors advised Paola that it was vital she make herself a priority to increase the chances of treatment success, so she embarked on a journey to improve every aspect of her life. This confluence of events started Paola down a different path of self-love, realizing that her cancer diagnoses were signs that she needed to alter her mental, emotional, physical and spiritual behaviours.

Her various oncologists were empathetic but direct – there was commonality in their main points, with all suggesting she needed to look after herself first and foremost. During appointments, they were inquisitive about her life and asked about work, recognizing immediately that Paola's stressful work environment was going to interfere with her treatment, with her breast cancer doctor saying:

"The world stops now, you're the priority of your life so we have to stop the stress from work, at home, everywhere. Your work needs to stop now, for at least one month after surgery – tell your employer you need one month off for surgery and recovery. You will see the world will continue and keep going with or without you. You have to really put yourself first. Everything outside of you stops now – love yourself and trust in God."

Coincidentally, whilst explaining the dangers of her treatment program for Non-Hodgkins lymphoma, Paola's oncologist concurred that, although it was a treatable disease, reducing stress was going to be key to a successful outcome, telling her:

"Treating this cancer is difficult and dangerous because the cancer cells are out of control and multiplying very quickly. You need to put yourself first, do what gives you the most peace and keeps you calm. Reduce as much stress from your life as possible. Your job is causing too much stress in your life. I will do my part to treat you, but you have to do your part, which is to make yourself the priority in your life, reduce the amount of stress in your life, otherwise the treatment is not going to work."

Paola's doctors also noticed it was her mum, not her boyfriend, who accompanied her to appointments, which lead them to ask about her private life and relationship, realizing how unhappy Paola was in her relationship. Her doctors said:

"Where you put your energy is where you put your focus and intention. If you're crying all the time about the relationship, it's not good for you because

that's where your energy goes – you need your energy to come back to you, to be healing your body. So, we need all that energy to heal."

The lack of involvement of her boyfriend during her cancer journey forced Paola to examine her relationship more closely and realized, like her job, this was a major stress contributor in her life. Paola ended the relationship during her second bout of chemotherapy and moved in with her mother, who looked after her during the difficult period of chemotherapy.

During treatment, Paola took a more introspective approach – rather than asking *"Why me?"* she asked herself: *"What do I need to learn from this?"* particularly as the type of Non-Hodgkins lymphoma she had was more common in women over the age of 60, and her symptoms were different from what was described online:

"I didn't understand why my body had this type of cancer. It was very confusing. I felt lost and, because of that, I thought the treatment wouldn't work for me because the internet said it worked for women over 60, which I wasn't. I realized this was my last chance in life to change and do something different, so I did. That's why I think I did everything I could to change my life."

Paola was also influenced by a well-known alternative medicine professional named Dr Santiago Rojas – a cancer survivor himself and well known in Columbia for exclusively treating cancer patients with alternative therapies to complement conventional treatment. Dr Rojas addressed Paola's low energy levels and advised that her stressful work situation needed to change saying: *"You don't get healed where you got sick."* Paola took this advice and applied it to every area of her life.

Paola decided to include a focus on self-love and self-care in her healing process which she says also played a key role in addressing various aspects of her life. She was heavily influenced by the documentary *Heal*, which focuses on the notion that the mind plays a major role in healing the body from dis-ease, and interviews physicians, psychologists, scientists, spiritual leaders and alternative medicine advocates whose messages heavily influenced Paola and her recovery journey. Whilst immersing herself in spiritual work with a therapist, Paola was advised to read a book called *Dying To Be Me* written by Anita Moorjani, who had a near-death experience whilst in a coma toward the end of her fight with lymphoma:

"That book was really interesting because the author says it was loving herself that changed her life – this opened my eyes a lot. For me, that became something that I knew I didn't know how to do, so it's been a huge life changing experience for me."

Paola acknowledges the profound influence that Moorjani's book now has on the way she lives her life, and credits the true account of Moorjani's near-death experience with helping her on the path of recovery from three cancers and to her new self, in which Paola began living life from a place of love and not fear – the lessons and messages about living life to its fullest resonated strongly with Paola and altered her perspective and focus. Paola now also includes regular meditation as part of her spiritual practice, saying:

"I still practice meditation every day, I visualize my body as healthy, and I talk to my cells and I tell those cells that I love them and will take good care of them."

On the work front, Paola also changed jobs to a role within the same organization, trading the previous toxic work environment for one with an amazing boss and supportive team, in a role which makes use of Paola's Master's Degree in Developmental Studies, and advising Government Ministers around issues relating to community health and well-being.

Whilst Paola addressed various personal relationships – leaving her boyfriend and shifting away from unsupportive friendships – she realized the biggest relationship she needed to change was the one she had with herself.

"The biggest relationship change I had was with the way I relate to myself. I started to meditate every day and I also started visualizing my healing and health. This all helped me change the relationship I had with 'me'. I started to find out that I didn't know how to love myself – I wanted to build that relationship and started learning about myself, getting in touch with myself, trying to really figure out what I want – and that changed a lot about how I began to relate to myself and, as a result, the way I relate to people. I left friendships that were not good for me, which brought me closer to the people who are really important and close to me in my life. My really close friends were there to hold my hand, were with me, visiting and comforting me. We were very tight. Also, the relationships with my family improved, especially with my dad. My dad and I were not very close, he was never one to talk too much, but he would always check on me every day to see how I was doing, and we became closer than we ever were before. I got to know him in a different way. Same with my two older brothers. They were there to help me through everything."

Paola's aggressive treatment program was completed in June 2020, and now consists of a daily breast cancer pill taken for the next five years, and she visits her doctor every six months for regular blood tests and scans as required. Her day-to-day priorities are exercising 30 minutes daily, eating healthily, continuing to focus on self-care, and living her life from a place of love, not fear.

Paola reiterates how much cancer taught her to change her perspective on living life, and how much she lived from fear in the past:

"In the stressful job that involved the harassment claim, I stayed there because I thought it was the only job in the world and I was afraid to lose it – I didn't

think I could get another job. I was living from fear. But when you live from love, everything changes. When I told my doctor 'I don't know how to find a new job, I don't have any hair on my head from chemo, I don't have any strength in my body right now, I feel like I can't go to a job interview', he told me: "If you decide to do it from love, it's all going to flow and the right job is going to come to you", and it happened – I bumped into my ex-colleague, she told me to come and work with her. This came from love, and I took the job. I kept myself in the previous stressful job because I was afraid to lose it. But now I understand there was something even better waiting for me. Your energy changes when you live from love."

This attitude also extended to Paola's personal relationships, which helped her leave the partner who was unsupportive during her treatment:

"I cannot be with a partner because I'm afraid I'm going to lose him, which was another thing I had to learn. I was putting him first, his needs, his issues, and I was overlooking all the red flags because I thought I was never going to find someone as good as him – all that was from fear."

Paola continues:

"Looking after myself is number one, but it's also an intense challenge because I feel healthy again and I'm trying to get my life back. I'm starting dating again. I have done a lot of personal learning and I know I need to be 'first'. It's been an amazing journey and I've started to put some limits in my work life. I love this job but if it's stressful, I will resign – I'm not putting my health at risk anymore. When it stops being fun, I'll go."

Paola lives her life as authentically herself as she can, honoring herself with personal wellness, self-love and self-care the main driving forces. She chose to remove fear from her decision making and lifestyle choices and, instead, made decisions that were based around self-love and self-care, carrying herself with a different energy and greater inner peace – fear has less control over her life:

"I feel great about myself now, I enjoy myself a lot, I know I'm great company, I have a lot of nice moments in my life. I started doing a lot of things I love that I didn't do before because I was busy. Now I feel better about myself. I feel living my life from love has healed me, and that's so important to do."

Paola is aware of the purpose and timing of cancer in her life, forcing her to look more closely at all aspects of her life and make necessary changes:

"Cancer was an amazing gift. I looked deep inside, and I found love – for my family, my friends and for myself. Cancer is a gift and it's also your body telling you that something is wrong – my body was saying to me: 'I love you so much that I need you to pay attention to me and to you.' When I started to heal myself, my soul and my body said: 'This is the way to heal.'"

17. "It's like living with a loaded gun to my head. It will come back, I just don't know when."

Paola Marra
London, United Kingdom
1 October 2022

How much does being happy and content matter in life? Do low moods, isolation or discontentment in life increase one's chances of developing cancer? These are some of the questions raised by breast cancer survivor and, now incurable stage 4 bowel cancer sufferer Paola Marra from London, UK.

Scientific studies around the influences of diet, weight and smoking on cancer are plentiful, but there's little to no evidence about the impacts of unhappiness or discontentment as variables potentially increasing the risks of acquiring cancer. The medical community considers it rare for someone under 50 to be diagnosed with both breast cancer and bowel cancer and Paola, also a fibromyalgia sufferer, wonders if there had been other causes at play for her:

"There are the genetic connections and cell mutations and all of those links, but I also think there are things that they can't measure, like stress probably has a massive impact. I think the way we live in terms of not just diet, weight,

smoking and exercise because they know that there are links to that, but I think being happy and content and all the things that we don't really talk about, all of that must have an impact. There's got to be links between your stress levels, happiness, that kind of stuff. And I know there's a real connection with trauma and fibromyalgia, so I don't see why there wouldn't be a connection between depression, trauma, and cancer. There's got to be something. I just don't know how they'd ever measure that type of thing."

Paola left her native Canada at the age of 18 to travel through Europe, eventually settling in London to focus on working within the music industry which she'd left to begin training as an architect. However, at age 47, whilst living in Cornwall in 2017, Paola was diagnosed with hormone-driven stage 1, grade 2 breast cancer. Due to Paola's pre-existing fibromyalgia, doctors opted to treat her with anti-hormone drugs to shrink the tumor for eight months which was effective, followed by a lumpectomy and five weeks of radiotherapy. After around twelve months since diagnosis, Paola was considered NED (no evidence of disease).

Paola decided to leave Cornwall and move back to her North London house, which she'd missed. Like all cancer patients that had progressed to NED, Paola was aware that cancer recurrence was possible. She'd felt that having had breast cancer while based in Cornwall was isolating and wanted to be in London in case of recurrence and, in 2020, Paola felt extreme abdominal pain and noticed severe rectal bleeding. She was sent for CT scans which didn't pick up the *"grapefruit-sized"* tumor inside her intestines and was told there were no signs of cancer. Given UK-based lockdowns with the onset of COVID-19, getting appointments was difficult. Paola managed to secure a colonoscopy appointment through her private healthcare provider as well as a CT scan and other tests, which was when the tumor was found and stage 3C bowel cancer was diagnosed, progressing to stage 4 ten months later.

The extensive treatment for Paola's bowel cancer was painful and *"brutal"* compared to her breast cancer treatment just a few years earlier. Over the course of ten months, Paola's treatment plan comprised multiple hospital stays, three surgeries including one which removed the cancerous tumor and placed an ileostomy, another emergency surgery to untwist her colon which had become completely blocked due to severe adhesions and a further surgery to reverse the ileostomy and more adhesion correction:

"After the first two initial surgeries, I had six rounds of chemo 'Folfox' (5FU, Oxaliplatin and Leucovorin). Chemo for bowel cancer is quite different from breast cancer. You have a port in your chest and each chemo cycle takes approximately three days. They do the first lot of chemo for six hours at the hospital, then you're sent home with a pump attached to your port. Mine was a small ball (the size of a tennis ball) filled with 5FU that you have at home for 48 hours. Then you go back in and have it disconnected. It's quite a process which surprised me because I had only known people who'd been through chemo for breast cancer, which happens in one day at the hospital. After the chemo I had another surgery to reverse the stoma and correct more adhesions. It was really intense."

Paola's mental health was impacted by the process which included return visits to the hospital and navigating treatment and surgeries alone during the pandemic, making the process even more difficult, with only doctors and nurses to help her through:

"I don't think my mental health was especially good at that point because it was so quick and traumatic. There were so many emergencies and complications, and I was in the hospital all the time. I had dehydration, infections, and lots of issues, I was allergic to the adhesives on my stoma bag, so it kept falling off. And I didn't really get any help. I couldn't speak to anyone, there were no support groups, there was just nothing. I was sort of just thrown into this world and had to get on with it. I was just trying to find help anywhere."

Complicating matters was lower abdomen pain months later which was identified as Krukenberg tumors on Paola's ovaries, connected to the original bowel cancer – unfortunately, the prognosis of patients with Krukenberg tumors is poor, with only 10% of patients surviving more than two years after diagnosis. Following more CT scans, PET scans and MRIs, Paola underwent a HIPEC/CRS with radical hysterectomy. They removed all female organs, belly button, Pouch of Douglas then scraped the peritoneum and omentum, then applied the internal chemo. HIPEC is where heated chemotherapy drugs are applied directly inside the abdomen to eliminate any remaining cancerous cells. Once the heated chemo was drained, Paola's abdomen was closed and stitched, and she was advised the expected recovery time from this type of surgery can take up to 12 months.

Paola felt very much alone during this process, noting the disparities between support for patients with breast cancer and bowel cancer – assistance is plentiful in the breast cancer community by comparison, whilst bowel cancer patients have much less access to support. Paola reasons this is because people are still embarrassed to talk about bowel cancer given the areas of the body and bodily functions affected. She felt an immediate connection with a lady named Deborah James in the UK, who was also called "Bowelbabe" and was the most vocal bowel cancer patient who raised awareness of the illness, bringing much-needed attention to the disease. Before her death at age 41 in June 2022, "Bowelbabe" was appointed Dame Commander of the Order of the British Empire (DBE), with her Damehood conferred on her by Prince William at her parental home. She set up a Foundation, published a book, and released a clothing line. At the time of her death, her fundraising website had accumulated almost 7 million pounds to fund clinical trials and research into personalised medicine for cancer patients and supporting campaigns to raise awareness of bowel cancer.

"Bowelbabe was just like a powerhouse. She did a lot for the cancer world but especially for bowel cancer because that's what she had. It's a shame because there's just no conversation about bowel cancer the way there was with her. I find there's little support, although this is changing mostly thanks to Deborah."

During down days whilst recovering from surgery in her North London home, Paola would watch Netflix alone with her dogs for hours as a coping mechanism and form of distraction. She praises hospital nurses for being available to her for chats during hospital stays, and credits her therapist for encouraging her to expand her networks via support groups and social media contacts, also recommending she visit Future Dreams, a breast cancer charity and support network based in Kings Cross, London, which Paola says helped her reconnect with other cancer patients and improve her social life:

"I've had cancer on and off for five years, so I've been in the world, I just haven't really made the connections. I go out all the time now and a lot of them are cancer people. I find the people I'm meeting now, I would never have met. We would never have crossed paths and only through cancer that we've met and I've had a brilliant time actually. It's really interesting how people from all different backgrounds and all different educations come together and there's no judgment. Now, because I'm feeling better, I try to go out as much as I can, I see friends, go out for lunch, or to events. But I try do things that I really want to do. If someone asks me to do something and I don't want to do it, I just don't do it. I see people who I find supportive and kind and caring. If there's something I really want to do and everyone is busy, I just go and do it. I'll go to an art gallery on my own, I'll go to see a film on my own. I'm successful at finding joy in every day. I really have some lovely moments and I think that's so important."

Many cancer patients and survivors comment on the fracturing that the word 'cancer' causes between the patient and existing friendships, however Paola finds that all friendships can be valuable, and cancer does not always need to be the topic of discussion:

"I think some don't talk about my cancer because they don't know what to say, and that's fine. I have people I can go to who can support me with cancer stuff. I still try to maintain friendships with people because I'm less intolerant than I used to be. And I think everyone has a value so even if they're not supportive and they only talk about themselves the whole time, I still think there's value in that maybe I can support them, it's not always about me. I believe you have different friends for different things, and I'd like to try to maintain those friendships. People have lives, people have problems, they have break-up issues, it can't always just be about cancer. Even though they're not going to die from a heartbreak, and I am going to die from my issue, it's still important to them and I think that's just what being a good friend is."

When it comes to talking about cancer with her friends, there is one question Paola prefers not to be asked:

"The one thing I don't like is people asking me how I am. I don't know how to answer that because, especially when you're going through treatment, it's such a massive question and do they really want the truth? Do people want to know that I spent five days vomiting up my own faeces? Do they want to know that? I don't think so! So don't ask me. I know the people who actually want to know, and the people who don't want to know, so I kind of adjust it. And sometimes I just don't want to tell people, so I just say 'I'm fine'. What is helpful is when someone sends a message saying: 'I'm thinking about you' or 'I'm going to pop by and bring you some food'. It's exhausting if you've got 20 people messaging 'How are you?' It's too much. It's kind that they want to know that you're OK, but it's a lot of work."

As Paola, reflects on her life before cancer, she recognises a different person in her younger self, and wishes she had the tools to live another way:

"I lived a life full of shame and I was so uptight about things that just do not matter. It almost makes me feel a little bit sad now because I think if I could have broken out of that, I could have done so much. There was no real support in my family, there was no encouragement. I didn't realize that you could do stuff, I didn't realize I could be an architect, I didn't realize I could travel. I just find it a bit sad. Life very much happened to me when I was young. I didn't kind of grab it and live it. Whereas now I'm living it. I'm very different than I was when I was younger."

In addition to spending more time with friends and amongst support groups, Paola has noticed that she lives *"in the now"* more than ever, particularly when delving more deeply into how she lived her life before cancer:

"My whole life, I've been scared of what people think of me, scared that people will 'see' me because I've had weight issues and stuff, so I didn't like people looking at me. If I hadn't been like that, I would have lived very differently. I still have some body issues, but now I just don't give a shit. I wear color, I used to live in black. I mean, it's unheard of that I'm wearing pink right now – people who knew me years ago would be like 'Oh my God, you're wearing color!' For me now, it's all about today, it has to be."

As to the future, Paola is now considered NED (no evidence of disease) which she finds difficult to comprehend given her stage 4 diagnosis, and all the previous treatments and surgeries she's been through:

"Right now, I'm considered NED again, although I am still stage 4 – it took me a while to get my head around this because, to me, NED means you're clear, but it doesn't mean that with stage 4, it just means that they can't see anything on a scan. So, they scan me and take bloods every three months. I've been having some pain which I thought might be my liver, but it's actually my pancreas. They found the type of cysts that can become cancerous and, in a normal person who doesn't have my history, they would just keep an eye on it by scanning once a year. But because it's me, and my body seems to like

cancer so much they're really keeping an eye on me, doing a lot more tests than they would with someone who's normal. Right now, today, I don't have cancer. It could come back in a week, it could come back in two years, they don't know. I find it difficult to live with because it's like living with a loaded gun to my head. It will come back, I just don't know when."

She's aware that palliative care will be required at some point and, in her usual head-on style of dealing with issues, Paola has made plans for what she sees as her inevitable future:

"I'm very much alone in this. Part of my fear is I'm going to die alone, that's my thing. My therapist suggested I go to a palliative care nurse to speak to her about dying and what happens practically, not just because I have a lot of fear about being in pain and being alone. Although a lot of people wouldn't like to talk about this, I feel like I need to because I am alone. It's been really helpful. I want to know what's going to happen. I think it would be scarier for me to go into it not knowing."

Until then, Paola continues to focus on living her life to its fullest every day, and admits she feels the happiest and most content now than she's ever been in her life, with more gratitude for 'moments' she didn't recognise before, understanding it took her cancer journey to acknowledge the importance of the littlest things in life:

"Strangely, I'm happier than I've ever been. I have more fun. I don't worry about what people think of me or necessarily what I look like. I just live. I live way more than I did. I'm much freer than I've been. And I have so much gratitude. Like, walking the dogs every morning in the park if the sunlight hits a certain tree and there's a bird there. I know it sounds so cheesy, but I'm just really grateful for those moments. Before cancer I was so caught up in stuff that didn't matter, that I wasn't able to recognize those moments. They were probably there the whole time and my eyes just weren't open to it."

∞ ∞ ∞ ∞ ∞

18. "Everything changed. My entire outlook on life changed."

Margaret Kennedy Hay
State of Washington, USA
8 October 2022

My chat with Margaret Kennedy Hay from Seattle, USA revealed a person whose life, personality, outlook and temperament were completely and forever changed by the cancer experience.

Margaret recalls the exact moment on that seemingly ordinary day in April 2011 when she was home alone, vacuuming the living room and preparing for guests to arrive for a regular Bible study meeting when a sharp abdominal pain forced her to collapse to the floor. With her husband out of town visiting his parents, Margaret drove herself to the local hospital emergency room located seven minutes from home and, in less than two hours, doctors discovered a volleyball-sized tumour and diagnosed her with uterine cancer.

The news came as a shock to then 44-year-old Margaret who'd attributed her mild symptoms to being perimenopausal, particularly as her routine gynaecological exam six months prior was all clear. Doctors have also said her type of cancer was rare for someone of her age, that it was more common amongst 65–70-year-old women.

Within days of the diagnosis, Margaret had a complete hysterectomy followed by six months of chemotherapy and radiation. Although tolerating chemotherapy without many side effects, Margaret did completely lose her hair which didn't bother her:

"I did lose all my hair and went completely bald. I really didn't care about that too much. I didn't wear a wig. I'm just one of those people who doesn't care what people think about me. Every now and again, I'd maybe put on a headband or wear a scarf, but I figured if somebody wanted to ask me about it, they could, and I'll tell them the story. I had a story to tell."

Married with two children, Margaret has always described herself as the caregiver: a stay-at-home mom involved in every aspect of her two children's lives as the *"PTA mom, the band mom and the football mom."* However, with the diagnosis and subsequent treatment, Margaret needed support to help her through the journey ahead, and says she felt immense gratitude for the wide range of assistance she received during the treatment period.

Her family rallied around: both children were at the University of Washington not far from home, her retired parents flew in and stayed with Margaret and her husband for six weeks, her brother and sister flew into Seattle with their spouses, and her husband quit his electrical contracting job to take care of her – essentially, her entire family basically put their life on hold. Margaret says she felt blessed with the outpouring of love, support, food, gift cards and financial aid with regards to daily bills from family, friends, local community and her church group members.

However, Margaret's 18-year-old daughter particularly struggled to come to terms with her mother's initial diagnosis – tears well up in Margaret's eyes when she recalls the mental and emotional effects suffered by her daughter during this stressful period, as the 18-year-old feared she'd lose her mother to cancer, which she relayed during heartbroken and tearful phone conversations:

"It's still raw for me, 10 years, 11 years later. It was very difficult for her, I had to get her into counselling. I was fighting for my life and trying to keep her going. It was her first year in college, 18 years old. And then, having her call me in the middle of the night sobbing hysterically and saying: 'Mama, please don't die. I don't know what I'll do, Mama if you die. I don't think I can go on.'"

Her high functioning autistic son was less of an open book, choosing to acknowledge his mum's journey via a cancer ribbon tattoo on his chest.

With all the surrounding help, Margaret fought hard within herself to maintain her position as caregiver within the family and mostly kept it together, but admits there were still times she wanted to curl up and scream:

"I remember when my daughter came over and – she and I knew my hair was going to fall out – she said, 'I'll come over and I'll shave your head'. About three or four days before she came over, I was washing my hair in the shower and I started to scrub my head – a big handful of hair came out, and I sat down in the shower and just cried. I couldn't do it in front of anyone because I'd always been the strong one for everybody – I just felt like I wasn't able to do that in front of anybody, ever. And really, the whole time that I had cancer, I never did it in front of anyone. And I can remember one time with my husband we had just like the most ridiculous fight, and I got so angry with him and, about my cancer, I just said 'You have to just let me be mad about this. I'm so damn mad.' But he couldn't understand. And it just made me mad that nobody could understand why I was angry."

Looking back on these events, Margaret has this advice for the family and friends trying to help a loved one through cancer:

"I think they just really need to give permission for whatever the patient needs to feel – if it's anger, if they're hurt, whatever it is, let them feel their feelings.

And feel it with them. Just be alongside them. It's not always going to be comfortable. It's hard, it's hard for everybody."

When Margaret's cancer struck, she and her husband were adjusting to married life as empty nesters, as their two children were now attending university. Margaret admits the timing of her cancer changed everything about their marriage and the life they'd shared:

"Once our kids went to college, I honestly think we were almost on the verge of a divorce. Because I had been so involved in their lives, my husband and I really didn't know who we were as a couple at that point. I think the cancer was a catalyst to kind of flip the switch for us. It has been such a growing experience for us. I think if we had not been through my cancer together, we would not have the marriage we have today. In that respect, I'm actually grateful for it which probably sounds kind of crazy, but I've said that to him and he said the same thing: that we're both kind of grateful because it really woke us both up to getting back to realizing how much we loved each other and how scared we were of possibly losing each other. Facing your own mortality is pretty damn terrifying."

In addition to redefining her relationship with her husband, Margaret admits cancer significantly impacted every aspect of her life:

"Everything changed. My entire outlook on life changed. I basically live for the moment now because I don't know what's going to happen tomorrow."

During the recovery period, Margaret found comfort in music and art therapy, particularly drawing and quilting, which she continues to this day. She also sought the help of a counsellor based at her oncology centre and attended online group meetings through Harmony Hill, a non-profit retreat facility focusing on wellness which also has a cancer program to support those affected by the disease, including caregivers and health professionals.

She also addressed longstanding issues relating to her weight and general health, including removing all processed foods, sugar and artificial sweeteners from her diet and exercising more than she had in the past. Prior to cancer, Margaret weighed 300 pounds and has since lost approximately 100 pounds.

As with many cancer patients I speak to, Margaret is part of the group who feels that cancer was the best thing that happened to them, because it forced them to re-evaluate their lives. She agrees cancer was the catalyst that changed her into a completely different person with a renewed sense of purpose:

"I feel like it has opened up my heart. I feel like I now want to give of myself more and help people and get out there. I feel like I want to take care of people now more than I ever did before. It's like, 'What can I do for you now?' I have a ton of people in my life that need help right now, and I've been hopping around to those people. I've just recently taken on my grandkids in the mornings and afternoons before and after school. I just have a really full life with all that, and I enjoy it."

When coming across people who are caught up in negative attitudes, Margaret maintains a sense of compassion as she can see her old self in that person:

"I was that kind of person. I was the kind of person who would sit and pick people apart, and maybe look at another woman and say 'Oh, look at her hair or look at her big butt' or whatever – just find the negative and tear down. And now I would come across a woman and say, 'Oh my gosh, you have beautiful hair' – I just find something positive and compliment someone about it. I just want to put good out. There's so much negativity in the world. I feel like we need to be putting out what we want to come back."

As a self-described music lover, Margaret realizes at almost 60 years of age, that life is very short and can change in the blink of an eye – she and her husband (now working for an electrical contractor) strive to live for the moment:

"We want to enjoy our time. If I see something that I think I'm going to enjoy, I'm not worried about if am going to have money ten years down the road – for instance, if there's a concert I want to go to next week and the tickets cost $250, by God I'm going to that concert! I've become very impulsive that way, or if there's a trip, that sort of thing. If there's a family member I feel has an event that I need to be at – for instance, I have a niece in Arkansas that has a play at the end of the month, and I only have a very small window of time to get there, and the tickets are $400 and I can only go for four days, I'll go because she's only going to have these opportunities very, very few times. I'm not going to be around forever. I need to take the opportunities while I'm here."

Enjoying every possible moment of her life, Margaret's cancer journey taught her to prioritise her health and well-being – classified NED (no evidence of disease), Margaret still keeps up with her scans every two years, visiting her doctors if there are any signs that something may be wrong:

"I'm not paranoid at all, but if I think anything seems suspicious, I'm quick to see my doctors and ask them to take a look. I'm extremely close with my oncologist, we're quite good friends and we keep in touch. I have two oncologists, one here in my hometown and I had one at the Seattle Cancer Care Alliance. The one that is here in my hometown has a BBQ at his property every year that I go to, and then I still send my one in Seattle a Christmas card every year and thank her for saving my life."

Since her cancer journey over 10 years ago, Margaret now enjoys sharing her life with the love and joy surrounding her daily, and you can safely bet that Margaret is likely spending time with her two children, many grandchildren, or taking the weekend off in her RV with her husband on a last minute, living-in-the-moment trip away to a random destination.

∞ ∞ ∞ ∞ ∞

19. "I TURNED THIS WHOLE THING AROUND AND WORKED IT AS MOTIVATION FOR ME."

Mark Lees
California, USA
27 November 2022

During my conversation with stage 3 parotid gland cancer survivor Mark Lees from San Diego, California, USA, Mark quipped: *"I'm an energetic guy at 67, but I've got the energy of a 27-year-old."* And throughout the interview, Mark's enthusiasm and energy for life shone through bright and clear – he certainly did have the energy of a 27-year-old but also the wisdom and life experience of someone who'd lived a full life, including cancer diagnosis, treatment and recovery.

Mark was born in Detroit, Michigan and now lives in sunny San Diego, California – he has a Master's Degree in Psychology and works part-time as a therapist, helping people with addiction, recovery and mental health issues. For the past ten years, he's been an avid hiker and massive proponent of enjoying nature for its ability to soothe, manage and ease the symptoms of anxiety, mood disorders, mental health issues, substance abuse, or simply just feeling stuck in life. His approach to counselling is different from the norm, often meeting clients in a local park, outside in nature, and far from the confines of an office.

He lives in a community for people aged over 55-years and is commonly known as an outwardly positive guy. Upon hearing of his cancer diagnosis in 2021, many of his supportive fellow residents told him: *"If anyone can beat this Mark, it's you."*

Following surgery to remove the cancer, Mark experienced 33 sessions of radiation in 5 weeks, describing the experience as gruelling. The radiation was so tough that he was eating through a straw by the final week. Whilst Mark lost a drastic amount of weight due to losing all taste buds and the salivary enzymes responsible for breaking down food, he regarded the treatment and subsequent recovery process as a full-time job, adopting a *"warrior"* attitude:

"When my radiation guy told me I wasn't going to be able to eat, I was going to lose weight, it's going to be mentally tough, I said 'Bring it on, I'm welcoming it.' It became my 40-hour week job – it was my fight, and my purpose. I refused to lose to this disease."

Because Mark's energy levels were so low during this time, regular hiking was impossible, so he resorted to begin moving his body via small steps in his driveway or backyard, recognizing: *"When I hit that wall physically, that was tough because although I was good in my mind and heart, I wasn't good in my body."*

Mark developed his own strategies to ensure his mindset remained optimistic and, as part of his warrior attitude, talks further about the skills which helped him through the recovery process, providing advice for other patients who might be struggling to maintain any level of positivity:

"Even if you're told you have a certain amount of time to live, what a wonderful opportunity to take advantage of the time you have left. I was not told that but, when I first got the diagnosis, after I cried and panicked a little, I said: 'This is not going to beat me. This will not beat me.' Nobody wants a

needle stuck in their neck for a biopsy, that was not fun, but I knew that it was part of the journey, part of the purpose. So, I turned this whole thing around and worked it as motivation for me. I said I'm going to go through the steps. It's all about attitude, I totally believe it because I know people doing the opposite, they just lose right off the bat, they're done, they're defeated, then they have to see a lot of counsellors and are trying to at least uplift their mood to even get through their treatments. And it's not easy, but I do think it's all about attitude."

For those cancer patients specifically, Mark has this advice:

"They need to tap into their belief system, their spiritual side, their support system, and the people they love. Learn to understand the precious gift of time. There's always hope, there's inch-by-inch and there's step-by-step. It isn't the event that messes it up, it isn't the cancer diagnosis that messes it up, it's our thoughts about the cancer diagnosis. It's that huge story we spin in our head and that crazy-ass story we invent. It's also about connection with others and people support. Also, at the time, I was seeing a therapist who offered an active listening ear and professional support – I highly suggest counselling or therapy to get you through. Having people around you, people that can support you even if you don't want that support, at least they're in the room with you. And gather facts, gather information, get support – there's a lot of stuff available that people don't know about, so that's why I always say, just investigate and research and you have to advocate for yourself, always, always, always. You have to advocate or have somebody advocate for you."

Mark understands, through his experience, that feeling depressed can be part of the cancer journey. Having suffered bouts of depression before and during diagnosis and treatment, Mark discusses the importance of movement for the body and the need for a sense of purpose in life:

"I teach my clients: change the thought and move a muscle. When you get depressed, just get up and move around, even in your house, just move. If you

get depressed, you feel isolated, just move. And we have to stay active in service and have purpose, especially with cancer. Most of the people who were getting radiation treatment alongside me worked. One guy I became friends with said he could not go through this without working. He said 'I'm tired, I'm exhausted, but I have to go to work. It gives me that service and purpose.' I really believe our work is our service and purpose."

Mark's energy levels began returning around six months after his radiation ended, which is when he put his hiking boots back onto his feet and ventured into nature to assist with his continued healing. He also returned to counselling patients in his local park, even taking some on hikes with him as part of those sessions:

"I take people out into nature and counsel them and they feel the benefits of nature. When you get outside, you're loosening up. Some people don't like having to be within the four walls or in a controlled environment. It's effective just getting out in nature because you get those five senses engaged, and if those five senses start firing, that's healing you. As soon as they hear the birds singing and see people walking by and the river is flowing by, it's therapeutic."

Since his cancer journey, Mark also noticed his attitudes to friendships, relationships and even random human contacts changed, describing every contact he has with other people as richer than he realized before:

"I think the universe puts people in our life for absolute reasons. I really believe we meet people for a reason, a season or forever. I had a lot of people I met even through the medical community including a radiation nurse that I clicked with right away who was also a hiker. We attract what we radiate into the universe. Cancer put people on my path, and I think the universe puts people on the path for everybody. But sometimes we're not aware of it or we're not open to it, and we don't see it. But I know my attitude had a lot to do with this. I gained more people in support when I was diagnosed than I had before the diagnosis. I also became more open to hearing and talking to people. If I'd

met them on Instagram or they were old friends, I understood the importance of those people and just being open to it."

Like many cancer patients who have been on that journey, Mark's approach to daily life is much different after the experience, recognizing the value of every living moment, and not focusing on the trivialities that may arise day-to-day:

"I didn't let the minutiae bother me, I could see it as nonsense. I didn't tap into it, I didn't react. Because I learned that life is so precious, I was given another outlook, another opportunity and everything became just more connected for me: people became more connected. If I went to a gas station, I started saying 'Hi' to people more or I was kinder to people, and I was more open to what people might be going through."

Talking about these positive impacts, Mark continues:

"The entire experience just made everything brighter for me in my life, especially with people. And it made me reconnect with myself first – it all happens first with ourselves. When I counsel patients, I'm always talking about how it starts in our hearts first, that change is not going to happen just because we want it from somebody else, we have to change first. It made me more connected to even acquaintances in my life and I became very intimate and warm and affectionate with people in my life. I told friends I loved them – I've never done that before but there are friends I would tell 'I need to tell you "I love you", because you're in my life, you're important to me and I'm so grateful that you spend that precious resource that we all get is time.' I understood that we can get our health back, we can get our money back, we can get jobs back, we can get people back, but we cannot get time back. It's gone. It's valuable, it's rich. I'm much more people connected. We're all living on the earth and we're all in this for the same reason, there is no disparity or diversity, we're all connected somehow, so I learned that so much more."

Mark has also recently come across the book *Cancer, Stress and Mindset: Focusing the Mind to Empower Healing and Resilience* by Brandon LaGreca which resonated heavily, and which he also highly recommends to those embarking on their own cancer journey. The book acts as a supportive guide and begins early on in a patient's diagnosis, providing practical steps to deal with the stress and anxiety associated with a cancer diagnosis, helping the patient alter their mindset, even if the outlook is terminal.

There is no stopping Mark from achieving the dreams he still has in his future, including finishing the book he is currently writing, continuing hiking and spending time in nature. He will continue to counsel patients and, on the subject of work, reflects on a quote that his mum used to say: *"I will live, and I will die. I'll work until I can't."*

Regular check-ups and MRI scans also remain part of Mark's future and, just before Thanksgiving 2022, he received the phone call that his most recent scan showed no evidence of disease. Of hearing this news just before Thanksgiving, Mark says:

"It gave me an extra spring in my step that day because I was cancer clear. So, Thanksgiving was definitely much better."

Reflecting back, Mark can see how his mental approach to hiking also helped him through the cancer journey, and offers this final statement:

"I don't have the same energy I did before this whole thing. It's all mental anyway, hiking to me is mental. It's our drive to get out there, one step at a time. If the mountain gets challenging, I don't let it beat me. My personality and my drive get me through. We all have to look forward to things. If someone asked me how to help get through cancer, it's to always have something to look forward to. I'm looking forward to the next challenge. I'm 67 years old, I am not done. I've still got a lot to give and understand on this earth. It's so much richer now for me. Every moment is precious – you never know

when you're gonna get the phone call. You just never know when your time is authored. 'Life expectancy' is the day you go, it isn't some number the statistics pump out, so I appreciate that so much more, the gift of that."

20. "I'M VERY FORTUNATE AND VERY BLESSED THAT I FOUND WHAT I NEEDED."

Joe Fazzini
Indiana, USA
9 December 2022

In 2008, at the age of 49, corporate executive and long-distance runner Joe Fazzini, based in Indianapolis, Indiana, USA, found himself in the rare category of less than 1% of men who are diagnosed with prostate cancer under the age of 50.

Now, 15 years later and healthy, 64-year-old Joe describes his initial diagnosis as a total fluke, having originally sought treatment in 2008 for a twisted ankle. Whilst treating Joe's ankle, his doctor suggested also taking full blood work which showed elevated and *"through the roof"* PSA levels – the PSA test is the primary test used to screen for prostate cancer. A biopsy was performed by a urologist less than one week later, with stage 3 prostate cancer diagnosed.

Two weeks later, on Joe's actual 50th birthday, an 8-hour prostatectomy surgery was performed and, although doctors told Joe the surgery was successful and the cancer had been removed, the cancer returned nine months later.

Despite having had complete faith in the medical team that was part of the initial diagnosis and surgery, Joe decided to take a more proactive approach towards the care relating to this return diagnosis, and changed urologists, believing: *"I've lived with the idea that I'm not responsible for my disease, but I am responsible for my own recovery."*

With that philosophy in mind, and also influenced by athletes like Lance Armstrong who had sought the best specialists at IU Health University Hospital in Indiana to treat their prostate cancer, Joe made an appointment with one of the top urologists at the Hospital. Immediately following their first meeting Joe began a course of 39 radiation sessions over six weeks as well as ADT (Androgen Deprivation Therapy) which involved infusing the well-known prostate cancer treatment drug Lupron (considered the "gold standard" for prostate cancer treatment) to suppress testosterone levels, essentially depriving the body of testosterone to stop the cancer from growing – testosterone is part of the Androgen family of male sex hormones, a known culprit that contributes to tumor growth and progression.

In the final three weeks of radiation, Joe was hit hard by extreme fatigue, no doubt due to the combination of radiation and the newly introduced Lupron medication. And although doctors believed the combination would treat the cancer successfully, it didn't work, and the cancer was still present. The following recommendation was grim; Joe was advised that the only option was to remain on Lupron for the rest of his life in order to keep Joe's testosterone at a minimal level which limits the supply that feeds the cancer's growth.

While Joe had faith in his doctors and the treatment plan suggested he underestimated what this treatment would do to his energy.

He continued running during all treatments, even when fatigue and weakness had a stranglehold over his energy levels, however admits it became almost impossible at times. With the encouragement of his doctors who'd recognized the importance of maintaining physical activity, Joe continued:

"I had already been trying to run while I'm on these treatments and there were some days that I couldn't even run a mile during that time period, but the doctor always said 'I don't want you to stop. I do not want you to stop, no matter how hard it is. Keep going.' There were times even when I was trying to run that I would literally pass out because I was so weak. I'd wake up laying on the trail. But I'd wake up, dust myself off and finish it up."

Following eight years of Lupron-based chemical therapy, the Lupron was effective at keeping Joe's prostate cancer at bay, as evidenced by his undetectable PSA levels. Yet, the negative side effects of the therapy, and drastically reduced testosterone levels in his body, had accumulated and greatly impacted Joe's mental and physical health, particularly as testosterone plays an important role in regulating sex drive, bone mass, fat distribution, muscle mass and strength, producing red blood cells and increasing the likelihood of irritability, poor concentration, and depression:

"At this point I was miserable. I was on antidepressants, and I remember saying to my wife: 'If this is my life, I can't do this, I just can't do this anymore.' I was so depressed."

In an effort to change the hand he was dealt, Joe began conducting his own research into international prostate cancer clinical trials and discovered a trial in Denmark. This specific trial, coordinated by a female doctor with 25 patients, hit the bullseye with Joe. The trial used long distance endurance running to keep prostate cancer in remission. Furthermore, it did not include Lupron in the treatment program.

Anxious to discontinue Lupron, Joe presented the findings of this trial to his Indiana University urologist, and suggested he was capable of following this type of program given his history as a long-distance runner and endurance athlete for over 30 years. His doctor agreed to support Joe in trialing this program, which included taking Joe off Lupron to see how his body responded to long distance training (incorporating running, swimming and cycling) alone. Given the long-term effects Joe was suffering from eight years of Lupron, he felt this was his only option and worth a try. Joe firmly believes the long-term mental health impacts of ongoing drugs, particularly in his case with Lupron, are neither considered nor discussed enough when addressing patient care:

"The mental health aspects are so much worse most times. If somebody ever asked me again, what would I rather have: Surgery or chemicals? I'd say I would take surgery anytime. I can come back from the physical part of this disease but what those chemicals were doing to me mentally was harsh, it was just some of the darkest times in my life. Long-term Lupron therapy patients are known to fall into dark spots, and we don't hear enough about the impacts on mental health. But those last four years of the chemical therapy were harsh. I was skin and bones, I couldn't hold any muscle, I was weak, lethargic, just very down. Just what you'd consider when you look at a guy who was in a very depressed state."

For the first time, Joe felt that he was controlling his destiny and he dove head first. He trained heavily with a coach and local triathlon group in Indiana called Tri-Loco, with his eyes firmly focused on IRONMAN® training. This proved to be an entirely different challenge because, although Joe had been a long-distance runner since the early 1970s, the transition to IRONMAN® status wasn't easy for any normal athlete, let alone an athlete with extremely low-level testosterone for the past eight years. To make matters worse, the Lupron destroyed much of Joe's bone calcium which led to a broken vertebra, stopping him from running for four months while it healed. Swimming and cycling compensated during this time, but Joe was well aware of the precautions he needed to take given the sustained impacts of Lupron:

"The Lupron took a big toll on my body which included bone fractures, and I developed an osteopenia, which I still have today. I have to be very cautious while I'm training. Lupron deteriorated my body quite a bit."

Nothing could stop Joe. He remained adamant that endurance training was the most ideal treatment for his situation. He was vigilant with his PSA-level blood testing and discovered at each subsequent test – from 90 days, six months, nine months – his high PSA levels didn't return, and his prostate cancer has remained in remission since he began the endurance training program.

Soon after, Joe completed his first IRONMAN® at aged 57, then his second at 61. He is also a two-time IRONMAN® finisher (Arizona, 2017 and Louisville, 2019), a seven-time 70.3-mile IRONMAN® finisher, has completed 20 full Marathons, including eight in Chicago, three in Los Angeles, two in Indianapolis, two in Carmel, Indiana and numerous eight-hour ultra-marathon events.

Joe recalls the course of action he took after his cancer returned nine months after surgery, emphatically changing doctors and following their recommended course of treatment including radiation and Lupron, yet became more proactive when the expected "all clear" results weren't delivered. Whilst replacing his traditional medically-based treatment program with long distance endurance training and an emphasis on a healthy lifestyle led his cancer into remission, Joe does caution readers, stating:

"I'm not saying don't do treatment. I don't want you to think that I said 'I'm just going to eat plants, exercise or do an herbal solution and that's my answer.' Not at all, there was none of that. When they said they were going to start infusing me with Lupron, I agreed and said 'Absolutely, if it's going to

keep me alive.' But I'm saying seek out your own answers. I just did some homework and I think everybody should do their homework. I don't want you to think I never did any of the medicine that was necessary."

To his doctor's surprise, Joe now attributes his remission status by starting IRONMAN® training and marathons, which is backed up by his continued undetectable PSA status and improved health statistics particularly around testosterone, which has increased from its Lupron-induced low level to within a normal range. Plus, his mental health greatly improved, leading his doctor to take him off antidepressants in 2018.

As our conversation shifted to treatment programs commonly utilized by cancer patients globally, particularly cannabis-based treatments, Joe says that including such alternative treatments in his program were not possible – Joe admits to overcoming substance abuse issues in his teenage years and including cannabis as part of his treatment would have increased the likelihood of a relapse. Instead, Joe continued regularly attending the recovery meetings he's frequented since 1983 and adhering to a 12-step program. He credits overcoming these substance abuse issues with the resilient attitude he lives with today, and which helped him fight cancer:

"Deciding I couldn't live with drugs anymore and fighting cancer were the two major turning points in my life. In fact, once I got out of surgery, I never took any pain medication, I never took a pain pill. I took Tylenol and I used the anti-inflammatories they gave me in the hospital. I'm very serious about anything that could trigger me into a relapse. I've watched a lot of people with cancer go the cannabis route through their treatments to take the edge off. I can't do that. I'm almost 40 years clean and sober and I don't want to lose that. It's very important to me to maintain that state. When I realized that I had to stay chemical-free once I was diagnosed with cancer, I knew that I had to change more than just keeping the drugs away. I had to change what I put

in my body – I had to sleep right, drink a gallon of water each day, and put the right type of nutrients into my body to stay healthy. I have a positive attitude, but I put a lot of work into the physical part of staying in remission as much as the mental."

Joe attributes much of his success to the support of his wife and family, but also believes being surrounded by additional support networks have helped in his recovery. Joe briefly attended cancer support group meetings in Indianapolis but realized these weren't the right fit for him, concluding he'd already had all the support he needed from his family, 12-step recovery groups, and his triathlon 'family':

"What also helps me is getting to work with other athletes who've got big goals – I found the type of people I want to be with outside of my nuclear family. There's 400 of us at the athletic club – those people are all younger than me for the most part, but they're enthusiastic about fitness. Their mental attitude keeps me excited. It's surrounding yourself with the right people. And it's not just once in a while – I need that type of reinforcement all the time, it keeps me focused."

As mentioned, a key source of support for Joe came from the 12-step program groups he'd been part of since the mid-1980s to address his substance addictions from the past:

"I've been to thousands of recovery meetings, and I was leaning on that fellowship to get me through my hard times. When you're going to a couple meetings a week, people can tell in those types of recovery environments when you're not doing good. I leaned on that fellowship during that time, and I leaned on my triathlon club when I wanted to get to an IRONMAN®. I'm very fortunate and very blessed that I found what I needed. But that's how I maintain my mental state – I had a recovery community that I could lean on."

Joe also acknowledges the support and guidance he received from the medical community in his recovery, stating:

"I'm extremely grateful for everybody that's been with me along the way. From 2008 to 2016 I had two urologists, a medical oncologist, radiation on-cologists, hundreds of nurses from the day I had surgeries all the way through to the doctor I still go to. And there's people drawing blood. I mean hundreds and I'm grateful for them all, they all served a purpose in my recovery. And that's why when I talk about taking responsibility for my recovery, I couldn't have done it without them."

In talking about his family and wife, who he has been with for over 38 years, Joe says:

"I've just been blessed with a great family, a great wife and that's what got me through a lot of it. And the idea that I wanted to be there for my kids, I wanted to be part of their lives. Knock on wood, I'm still here."

Looking back on his cancer journey, Joe recognizes that taking a pro-active approach to his treatment whilst also being vigilant about health, fitness and diet (Joe has been a vegetarian for 25 years and a strict vegan for over 16 years), he recognizes how fortunate he is:

"I've got a reputation out there for being tough as nails, but I'm just a big baby. But I'm out here plugging away, I'm trying my best. I always tell people I'm just lucky and they say: 'Oh you did all the right things.' But I know a lot of people that have had cancer that have also done all the right things and still not made it. I'm one of the lucky ones."

Furthermore, Joe believes a number of key attributes play an im-portant role in the recovery process, including:

"I do believe if you can stay active, if you have a good mindset along the way, and that you're willing to participate in your recovery – you don't have to be an IRONMAN®, but if people can get out and keep their body moving and put a little effort into it, rather than just laying on the couch and taking the treatments – eat right, sleep right, get some physical movement, and have a number of support groups."

After 39 years as a Corporate Executive, and now at 64 years of age, Joe finds himself seriously pondering the prospect of retirement and how he will spend his time during that next phase of his life:

"I now find myself in a situation where retirement is inevitable. I've done well and right now I'm doing minor consulting things. Plus, I get paid to coach, so there's some coaching fees. It'll never put me into the Jeff Bezos or Zuckerberg class of money, but it keeps the lights on. It's my encore. It's what I plan on doing into my retirement, becoming a professional coach and doing that full time. And I have started a book and I've got the first six chapters done."

However, like many cancer patients, Joe is quick to wonder if the latest pain in his body could be cancer returning even after remaining in remission for a number of years:

"It's never NOT on my mind. If I get a headache, I think it's a brain tumor. I always tell people the mental aspect of cancer never really goes away."

Joe's doctors recommend annual PSA testing but, as someone who continues to play a very active role in every aspect of his own health, Joe tests through his GP twice per year. So far, his PSA levels have remained at undetectable levels and he "high fives" his GP on the way out of each appointment, living his life full steam ahead until the next test, which includes endurance training and marathon running:

"When I show up at a race, they don't know my background, they just see this old guy with white hair coming out. They call me 'Iron Joe' because I seem to keep going no matter what. And that's my claim to fame. I'm not going easy. I don't know what else God can have in store for me, if between the drug addiction that I beat and putting cancer behind me, I don't know what can be next. But one thing I know is that time is undefeated, none of us get out of here unscathed so I'll just keep doing my best."

∞ ∞ ∞ ∞ ∞

ACKNOWLEDGMENTS

I would like to express my sincere thanks to the twenty courageous and wonderful individuals who were willing to share their personal stories with me for this book. Your bravery, strength and resilience in the face of cancer and openness during our discussions and communications both touched and moved me, and I'm grateful for the time we spent together chatting and communicating during the process.

My heartfelt and personal thanks for agreeing to my request for an interview to be featured in this book – as a non-journalist and pretty basic writer, thank you for your openness and trusting me with the privilege of telling this part of your life: Chris, Heather, Ann, Lauren, Dave, Vincent, Tom, Margie, Stuart, Marc, Judy, Stef, Kunwar Ujjwal, Tara, Mari, Paola B, Paola M, Margaret, Mark and Joe – individually, you've deeply impacted my life and opened my heart. Thank you for sharing your personal journey with me.

Thank you to Robert Henry for assisting with the preparation of the page design elements of the book.

Finally, thank you to my dear friends Nancy and Andrew Cover of CAN Design in Melbourne, Australia for handling the cover design of the book. We worked together on the first book and it's so special to me that you could be involved in this follow-up as well.

ABOUT THE AUTHOR

Richard Calautti is a researcher and marketing professional based in Perth, Australia. He is the creator of Live Life Now Project (since 2009), and can be reached via Instagram (@LiveLifeNowProject) or through his LinkedIn profile.

 LiveLifeNowProject

LiveLifeNowProject.com

Made in United States
Troutdale, OR
06/16/2023

10627325R00082